D1130089

BIOGRAPHY OF THE EARTH

Its Past, Present, and Future

REVISED EDITION

BY

GEORGE GAMOW

Professor of Physics
University of Colorado

NEW YORK

THE VIKING PRESS

FIRST PUBLISHED IN 1941 BY THE VIKING PRESS, INC.

FIFTH PRINTING 1953

REVISED EDITION

PUBLISHED IN 1959 BY THE VIKING PRESS, INC.

625 MADISON AVENUE, NEW YORK 22, N.Y.

PUBLISHED IN CANADA BY

THE MACMILLAN COMPANY OF CANADA LIMITED

SECOND PRINTING 1960

LIBRARY OF CONGRESS CATALOG CARD NUMBER: 59-11578

PRINTED IN THE U.S.A. BY THE COLONIAL PRESS INC.

Age followed age
As minute follows minute.
—Lermontov

DEDICATED TO

ρ

—R. Wagner

Preface to the Revised Edition

EIGHTEEN years have passed since the first edition of this book rolled down from the printing presses. Although that period of time is negligibly short from the point of view of the geological time scale, it turned out to be quite important in the time scale of the development of cosmogony.

A few years after the first publication of this book, a profound change took place in our views concerning the origin of the Earth, and of the planetary system in general. The collision theory of the origin of planets, which replaced the Kant-Laplace nebular hypothesis at the break of the century, is now definitely out, and we are back again to a modified and modernized version of the views of Kant and Laplace. It seems that this third reversal of cosmogonical views is now here for good, and that we are safe from any further radical changes in the basic ideas concerning the solution of that ancient riddle.

The present "parthenogenetic" theory of the origin of the planetary system gives us the assurance of the plurality of the inhabitable worlds; in fact, it now seems certain that at least one per cent of the hundred billion stars forming our stellar system of the Milky Way possess planets not much different from those revolving around our sun. And the recent developments in studies of the origin of life make it almost certain that some kind of life, probably not much different from our own, may exist in the millions of other inhabitable worlds.

In preparing the revised edition of this book the author faced a difficult problem of bringing it up to date without causing too many headaches to the publishers and printer. He hopes that he has solved the problem in a satisfactory way, and that the reader of the revised edition will accept it as old wine in a new bottle.

GEORGE GAMOW

University of Colorado
February 1959

Contents

Illustrations

PLATES

FIGURES

Note on Units of Measurement

IN THIS book the decimal metric system, universally employed in scientific research, is used. For those readers who are more accustomed to feet, pounds, and the Fahrenheit temperature scale, we give the following table of metric equivalents:

1 centimetre = 0.39 inch
1 kilometre = 0.62 mile
1 gramme = 0.035 ounce
1 kilogram = 2.20 pounds

To convert into Fahrenheit the temperatures here given in degrees Centigrade, multiply by $\frac{9}{5}$ and add 32 (e.g., 20° C. is the same as $20 \times \frac{9}{5} + 32 = 68°$ F.).

Data about the Earth

Polar diameter	12,713.8 km. (7883 miles)
Equatorial diameter	12,756.8 km. (7909 miles)
Total mass	5.98×10^{21} metric tons

CHAPTER I

The Age of the Earth

THE DATE OF BIRTH

"THE Earth was born in the year ——." This is how Chapter I is supposed to begin, according to the best traditions of biography. But, before filling in the

Figure 1
Egyptian version of the creation of the world. The god of the air, Shu, son of the Sun-god Amon-Ra, separating his sister Nut, the sky, from his brother Keb, the Earth. Amon-Ra himself was born of the lotus flower growing on the surface of the primordial ocean.

blank space, we might ask whether we may not assume that the Earth has existed through all eternity and has always been very much the same as we know it at present.

It seems, however, that the idea of the eternity and permanence of our world never appealed to the human mind, and from the very beginning of thought men have always tried to imagine some kind of *creative process* that made the world as it is now. Virtually all ancient religions—which were, essentially, the first attempts of the awakening intellect to find its place in the surrounding world—discussed the problem of creation at considerable length. The separation of the Earth from the sky by the Egyptian god Shu (Figure 1) and the familiar, elaborate system of Jehovah's six days of creation are typical of such attempts. In spite of their highly fantastic character, all these early cosmogonic systems contain one fundamental truth: *the whole universe, and our Earth in particular, were actually formed from previously unorganized matter, or chaos, in some far distant past.*

Astronomical evidence clearly indicates that *the multitude of stars we see in the sky—our own Sun among them—could not have existed eternally and were probably formed earlier than some five billion years ago from the hot primordial gas that previously filled all the universe.**

But, as we are chiefly concerned with our own little planet in this book, let us shrink our horizons and ask ourselves specifically about the age of the Earth. How long has the surface of the Earth possessed such familiar features as oceans, seas, land, and mountains, and how long can our globe have existed as an individual celestial body?

THE AGE OF THE OCEANS

Let us first turn to the oceans and seas that now cover nearly three-quarters of the surface of our planet. How long have they been in existence? To obtain the answer

* The problem of the "creation" and evolution of the stellar universe is discussed by the author in his book, *The Creation of the Universe* (New York, The Viking Press, 1952).

to this question, all one has to do is to swallow some water while bathing in the surf and then to think about it a while, the thinking, of course, being more important than the swallowing. Everyone knows that ocean water is salty, but few are aware that this salt was brought into the ocean by the so-called sweet waters of rivers and creeks during tremendously long geological epochs in the past.* Flowing across the Earth's surface in mountain streams, creeks, and rivers, water slowly wears away even the hardest rocks, carrying their substance into the seas and oceans. The insoluble parts, carried along by rivers as a thin suspension and giving the water a muddy appearance, are deposited on the bottom of the sea in ever-growing layers of sediment. The salts remain in solution and steadily increase the salinity of ocean water. Under the action of the rays of the sun, great quantities of water evaporate from the ocean's surface and fall back on the earth in the form of rain or snow, to begin their undermining work all over again, but the salts remain permanently in the ocean.

The fact that the present salinity of ocean water is only about one-tenth of what would correspond to saturation is conclusive proof that this accumulation of salt required a finite period of time. If we divide the total quantity of salt now dissolved in the ocean by the amount that rivers carry into solution annually we can get a figure for the age of the oceans themselves. The quantity of salt dissolved in the oceans can be readily estimated from the total volume of ocean water (1,500,000,000 cubic kilometres) and the measured salt concentration (3 per cent). The result is a tremendous figure. If we could extract all

* As we shall see later (p. 146) geological evidence clearly indicates that during the early periods of their existence the oceans consisted entirely of sweet water.

this salt, it would form a solid block about 20,000,000 cubic kilometres in volume (the size of a cube 270 kilometres on each edge), weighing more than 40,000,000,000,000,000 tons! On the other hand, geologists have estimated that rivers carry about 400,000,000 tons of salt into the ocean each year. Assuming that such washing out, or *erosion* as geologists call it, has always proceeded at the present rate, we must conclude that the oceans and seas have existed for about one hundred million years.

It is probable, however, that the present rate of erosion is considerably higher than the average rate during past geological epochs. As we shall see later, the present features of the Earth's surface, with its numerous towering mountains and high plateaux, are not at all typical of the average state of the Earth. Such features exist only during comparatively short intervals immediately following the catastrophic events of mountain formation caused by the slow shrinking of the Earth.* During long intervals of geologic time, when the previously formed mountains were almost completely washed off the face of the Earth by the destructive action of water and new mountains had not yet risen, the surface of our planet was flatter and much less picturesque than it is now, with vast areas covered by shallow seas. In such periods not much land was exposed to erosion, and the rivers carried salt to the ocean at a considerably slower rate. Moreover, some of the salt carried into the ocean may have been removed by subsequent elevations of submerged lands. If this is so, some of the river-borne salt is now simply returning to the ocean and must be deducted when calculating the total.

Since these corrections raise the age of the oceans, as

* *Cf.* Chapter VI.

estimated above, some ten or even fifteen times, we must conclude that *the great bodies of water on the surface of the Earth were formed about one or, more probably, one and a half-billion years ago.* But this definitely represents the upper possible limit. If the oceans had existed for a much longer period, they would now all be as salty as the Dead Sea or the Great Salt Lake!*

Before that time all the Earth's water must have existed solely in the form of atmospheric vapour, which implies that *the surface of the Earth must have been extremely hot.* Only after the surface temperature dropped below the boiling point of water did unprecedented showers fall from the sky on the rocky surface of the young planet, filling all depressions and forming the vast oceans and seas we find today.

THE AGE OF THE ROCKS

But what about the rocks themselves, which form the solid crust of our planet? Is there a way of estimating their age? Yes, and a very good way indeed. Although at first sight rocks exhibit no changeable features that tell their age, many of them actually contain a sort of natural clock, which, to the experienced eye of the geologist, indicates exactly how long ago a certain rock solidified from its former molten state. This age-betraying geological clock is represented by the minute amounts of the so-called radioactive elements, uranium and thorium, often found in various rocks taken from the surface or from the depths of the Earth.

The atoms of uranium and thorium are the heaviest

* It may be observed here that salt lakes were formed by the evaporation of great bodies of ocean water left on the continents as the result of the recession of the seas.

of all existing atoms and possess the peculiar property of instability, slowly disintegrating and emitting their constituent parts. These splinters, ejected with extremely high velocities from the unstable atoms of radioactive elements, are called *alpha-particles* and actually are the nuclei (or atomic cores) of ordinary helium atoms. Losing these constituent parts one by one, radioactive elements pass through a number of intermediate stages and end up as the atoms of the common element lead.

Although the rate of radioactive decay of uranium and thorium is extremely low, it can be measured accurately by counting the number of alpha-particles emitted by a given amount of material during a given interval of time. Such counting is made possible by the use of an extremely sensitive instrument of modern experimental physics, known as the Geiger counter, which registers each alpha-particle, that is, each single atomic transformation.

It was found that one gramme of uranium yields $\frac{1}{7,600,000,000}$ gramme of lead annually, the corresponding figure for thorium being $\frac{1}{28,000,000,000}$ gramme. Hence it is easy to calculate that it takes 4,500,000,000 and 16,500,000,000 years, respectively, for any given amount of uranium and thorium to be reduced to one-half its size, twice as much time to reduce it to one-quarter, three times as much time to one-eighth, and so on. The rate of radioactive decay remains remarkably constant with time and independent of the pressure and temperature as well as of the chemical constitution of the surroundings,* so

* In fact, the German physicist Carl von Weizsäcker has calculated that these heavy elements would have to be subjected to the temperatures of several billion degrees and pressures of several billion atmospheres to influence their rate of transformation.

that radioactive substances represent the most dependable type of time-measuring instrument in the world.

To determine the age of any given rock containing uranium or thorium we need only measure the amount of lead that has accumulated in the rock as the result of radioactive decay. Yet, as long as the material forming the rock was in a molten state, the products of disintegration must have been continuously removed from the place of their origin by diffusion and convection. But as soon as the material solidified into rock, the accumulation of lead alongside the radioactive elements must have begun, so that the observed degree of deposition should give us exact information about the time elapsed since solidification took place.

Applying this method to igneous rocks found in the deposits formed during various geological eras, geologists were able to develop a rather exact chronology of the events which took place on the surface of the Earth in the distant past. Since, however, none of the rocks forming the crust of the Earth were found to be more than two billion years old, it was concluded that prior to that date the entire body of the Earth was in a completely molten state.

During recent years this figure for the date of the formation of the Earth's crust has been considerably modified, due to a new method of measuring geological age. The point is that the sequence of the radioactive products leading from uranium to lead contains one link—radium emanation or radon—which is a gas and can diffuse away from the place of its origin even after the material becomes solid. The diffusion of this gas reduces the amount of lead deposited in the immediate neighborhood of uranium. Consequently previous estimates of age of the rocks proved to be too low.

A much more accurate date can be obtained by studying the decay of another unstable chemical element known as rubidium, which slowly turns into strontium during the period of 430,000,000 years. Since both rubidium and strontium are solids, no losses caused by gaseous diffusion through the rocks are to be expected, and the amount of strontium deposited near rubidium should give the correct date at which the rock solidified. The use of this more reliable method more than doubled the estimated age of various rocks and raised the figure for the date of formation of the Earth's crust to about five billion years ago. Thus the pedantic reader may now turn back to page 1, and insert the year 5,000,000,000 B.C. in the blank space for the Earth's birth date.

CHAPTER II

The Blessed Event

WAS IT A COMET?

NOW that we have the Earth's date of birth and its mother's name, the next natural question to ask is: "Who was its father, and exactly how did it all happen?"

The first attempt to answer this question was made about two centuries ago by the celebrated French naturalist Georges-Louis Leclerc, Comte de Buffon, in one of the forty-four volumes of his *Histoire Naturelle,* which is probably the most brilliant and comprehensive study of natural science ever written. Buffon described the formation of the planetary system as the result of a violent collision between the Sun and some foreign celestial body which he called a "comet." His use of this word for the "father" body that caused the birth of our Earth was certainly due to the lack of contemporary knowledge about the nature of comets rather than to any doubt in his mind concerning the kind of body required to produce the effect. We know now that comets actually contain extremely small amounts of matter, in spite of their resplendent appearance and tremendous length; they are pithily characterized by Prof. Henry Norris Russell as "airy nothings." (Plate IIA). Their seemingly bulky heads most probably consist of a loose swarm of small meteorites with a total mass hundreds of thousands of times less than that of the Earth, and their beautiful tails consist of an extremely rarefied gas with a density a million times smaller than that of atmospheric air. The collision of such a comet with our Earth would scarcely result in anything more than an exceptionally brilliant meteoric display. What Buffon actually meant, as can be seen from Figure

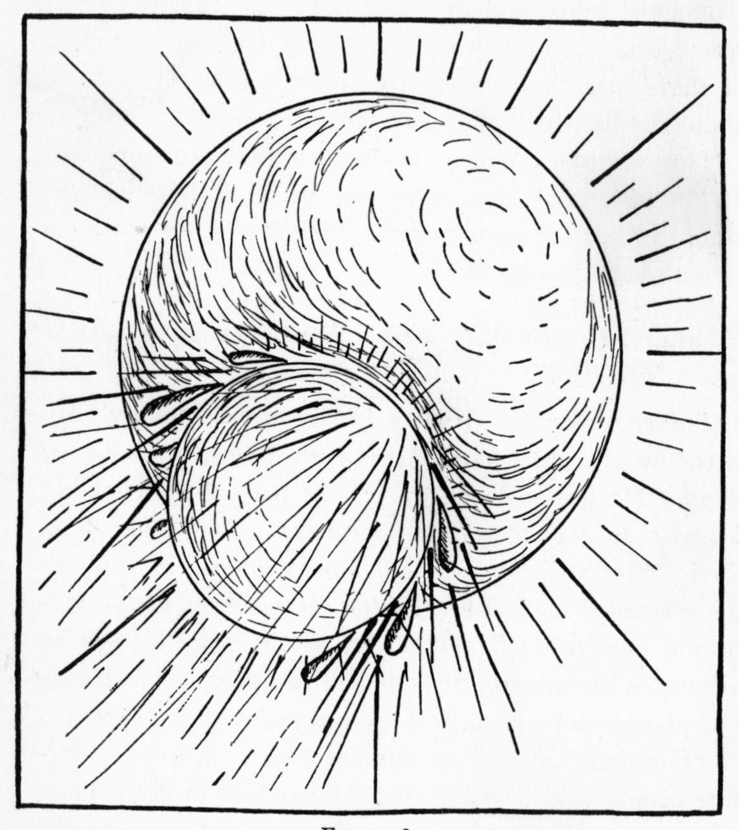

FIGURE 2
The collision between the Sun and a passing star (after Buffon).

2, drawn after an illustration from his *Natural History*, was the collision of the Sun with another star of comparable size.

As the result of this violent impact between the two

parent stars, various-sized bits of stellar matter must have been thrown out from the two gigantic bodies, and (if the collision was not exactly head-on) the whole system must have been set in rapid rotation. Some of the collision fragments were probably lost for ever in interstellar space, while others, held by the gravitational attraction of the central body, were forced to continue revolving about the Sun in the form of separate planets.

This would explain in a wholly natural manner why all the planets of our system revolve in almost the same plane, and in the same general direction of the Sun's rotation about its own axis.

COULD THE PLANETS HAVE BEEN BORN WITHOUT A "FATHER"?

These cosmogonic views of Buffon were violently criticized by the celebrated French mathematician Pierre-Simon, Marquis de Laplace, in his book *Exposition du Système du Monde,* which appeared in 1796, eight years after Buffon's death. Laplace's chief criticism of Buffon's views stressed the fact that matter ejected from the surface of the Sun in such a collision would have to revolve around it in greatly elongated elliptical orbits, whereas the planets pursue, as we know, almost circular paths.

To replace Buffon's "two-parent theory," Laplace therefore proposed the theory* that the Sun produced the planetary system "all by itself," as the result of a terrific internal explosion that threw a part of its atmosphere far beyond the present orbits of the planets. *"This explosion,"* writes Laplace, *"might have taken place through causes similar to that which produced the brilliant out-*

* Borrowed from Immanuel Kant.

burst in 1572, lasting several months, of the famous star in the constellation Cassiopeia." Translated into modern language this would mean that the planetary system was

FIGURE 3
A slowly rotating acrobat begins to spin very fast by pressing her arms alongside her body. (Drawing after Degas.)

formed as the result of the Sun's having become a nova or supernova in the distant past.* Since Laplace's theory did not include a collision with another star, which might have set the entire system in rotation, he was forced to

* The phenomena of the nova and supernova are vast stellar explosions increasing the original luminosity of a star by a factor of a millon or (for supernova) even by a factor of a billion.

assume that the Sun rotated at the very beginning of its existence and that a part of this rotation was transferred to the extensive atmosphere formed by the explosion. After the original force of the explosion had spent itself, the gradual cooling of this giant gas sphere, caused by radiation of heat into interstellar space, must have resulted in a steady contraction. It is well known, however, that the contraction of any rotating body leads to an increase in its angular velocity. This phenomenon can be observed at the circus when an acrobat, lazily rotating on the end of a rope, becomes a glittering whirl after she folds her previously extended arms across her breast (Figure 3).

This well-known trick demonstrates one of the fundamental laws of mechanics: *the law of conservation of rotational momentum*. Rotational momentum is defined as the product of three factors: the mass of a rotating body, its linear velocity, and its distance from the axis of rotation. In the case of our rotating acrobat, the rotational momentum of her arms, for example, is given by the product of their mass, their length, and the velocity of rotation, as indicated by the arrow in Figure 3. When the arms are brought close to the body, their distance from the axis of rotation decreases, and, to maintain a constant rotational momentum, their velocity must increase. Since the arms are part of the whole body and cannot move separately, however, this increase of velocity must be equally distributed between the arms and the rest of the acrobat, so that the whole body must spin faster.*

* Hence the increase of rotational velocity will be especially great in the case of a very thin acrobat with extremely heavy hands. Holding heavy objects in the fists will also increase the acrobat's rate of spin.

According to the Kant-Laplace views, this is exactly what must have happened to the contracting Sun. Since the spinning Sun was not so rigid as the body of an acrobat, one might expect that the centrifugal force would separate rings of solar matter from the elongated solar equator. Such ring formation can be demonstrated by the classical experiment (Plateau's experiment) in which a large spherical mass of olive oil suspended in some other liquid of equal density (for example a 50-50 mixture of water and alcohol) is brought into rapid rotation by means of paddles attached to a vertical axis and driven by an electric motor. As the speed of rotation increases, the oil sphere becomes more and more ellipsoidal, and at a certain speed the rings of oil begin to detach themselves from its equatorial bulge. Almost instantaneously after their formation, the rings break up, forming large globules of oil of various sizes.

It is interesting to notice that neither of the two creators of this theory of the origin of the planetary system subjected it to a mathematical treatment. In Kant's case this is not surprising; he was just a philosopher, and was not indoctrinated in the art of mathematical analysis. But Laplace was one of the greatest mathematicians of all time, and the fact that he discussed this theory in a semipopular book deprived of any mathematical formulae and never referred to it again in his more professional publications may suggest that he had tried to give the theory a mathematical formulation but failed to do so.

MAXWELL'S CRITICISM

One way or another, the first mathematical analysis of the Kant-Laplace hypothesis was carried out by the famous

British theoretical physicist James Clerk Maxwell, the founder of electrodynamics. In a paper published in 1859 Maxwell investigated the stability problem of the Saturn rings. It was known in his time that Saturn's rings are not thin solid disks similar to gramophone records, but consist of billions upon billions of small bodies of various sizes (maybe from the size of a sand grain to the size of Mount Everest), rotating in one plane around the planet. Why didn't this dispersed material forming the ring condense under the forces of mutual gravitational attraction into one or several large bodies to be added to the already existing nine satellites of Saturn? According to Maxwell's mathematical analysis, there are two opposing forces which have to be considered in this case:

I. Gravitational attraction between the particles forming the rings, which tends to condense them into just one or a few large bodies.

II. The shearing forces due to different angular velocities of different parts of the ring, which tend to break up any such condensation as soon as it begins to form. In fact, as would be expected theoretically and as is also confirmed by direct observation, the outer parts of the ring rotate more slowly than its inner parts, so that the latter would tend to run away from the former if the material of the ring were to be collected into one single satellite.

Maxwell had proved, by strict mathematical analysis, that in the case of Saturn's ring, the shearing forces opposing the condensation of the particles forming the ring into a single body are much stronger than Newtonian attraction between the individual particles, so that the condensation of the ring into one or more satellites can never take place. This explained to his satisfaction the fact that

Saturn's rings are a permanent feature of that planet.

But the rings which were presumably formed around the sun and, according to the Kant-Laplace hypothesis, condensed into the planets were similar to the rings which encircle the planet Saturn today. Could they have condensed into planets, as Kant and Laplace presumed? According to Maxwell's calculations the possibility of such a condensation depends on the amount of material present in the ring. If there is not enough material, as in the case of the Saturn rings, the forces of gravity tending to condense the ring into a single spherical body are not strong enough, and the rings remain rings. If, however, the total amount of material is large enough, the ring is bound to break into one or more large spheres.

What was the situation in the case of the original material forming the giant ring around the young Sun? Could it condense into planets, or couldn't it? To answer that question, Maxwell took (theoretically!) the combined mass of all the planets of the solar system and spread it out uniformly all over the plane of the elliptics, thus forming the distribution of material which presumably existed before the planets were formed. Applying his mathematical criterion to this hypothetical primordial ring around the Sun, Maxwell found that it could not possibly have condensed into planets because, in this case, the matter of the ring was so diluted that gravitational attraction between its different parts was helpless against the shearing forces which tended to break up any condensation at its very start. In fact, Maxwell was able to prove that the ring around the sun could not have condensed into planets unless the amount of the material in it had exceeded the combined mass of all planets by a factor of about 100.

The result of Maxwell's calculations forced the astronomers to abandon the Kant-Laplace hypothesis and to return to the original collision hypothesis of the Comte de Buffon. The modernized form of the collision theory was formulated in the beginning of the present century by Sir James Jeans in England, and by Thomas C. Chamberlin and Forest R. Moulton in the United States. Accepting Buffon's view that the birth of planets was due to some foreign body from interstellar space, this new version abandoned the concept of a direct material collision, substituting the view that the planets were formed as the result of a giant tide raised on the surface of the Sun by the gravitational attraction of an intruding star as it passed at a distance of, maybe, only several solar diameters. The phenomenon of tides is familiar to everyone who has spent some time at the seashore. In the case of the Earth's liquid envelope, they are observed as the periodic rise and fall of ocean waters caused by combined action of the Moon and the Sun. This effect is due primarily to the uneven attraction exerted upon the different parts of the body in question by another disturbing body and is illustrated in Figure 4 on page 18.

Since the force of gravity decreases with the square of the distance (Newton's law), the material situated on the side of the sphere facing the disturbing body (c) is attracted more strongly than the material in the centre (b) which in turn is attracted more strongly than the material on the opposite side (a). The resulting difference of forces tends to elongate the body in the direction of the attractive forces, and if it is deformable it takes the shape of an elongated ellipsoid. In the case of the Earth, tidal forces produce their strongest effect on the liquid envelope, giving rise to two tidal waves on opposite sides. If the disturbing body is not very close, as, for example, in the case of the Earth and the Moon, the disturbance will possess a symmetrical character and both tidal waves will be of about the same height. If, however, the distance decreases, the tidal wave on the front side will become considerably higher, and the matter composing the front

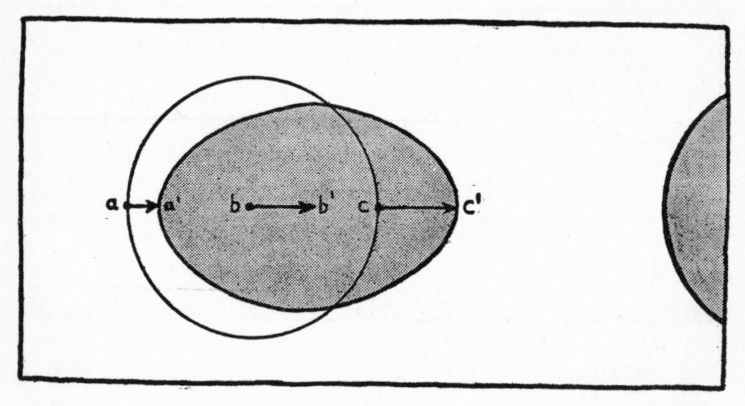

FIGURE 4
Action of tidal forces on a deformable body.

crest of the tidal wave may be entirely separated and break away into space toward the disturbing body. In the case of ocean tides, this would correspond to water splitting off from the top of the tidal wave directly toward the Moon, if the latter happened to come too close! According to the tidal hypothesis of Jeans and Chamberlin and Moulton, something similar happened to our Sun when the intruding star came too close to its surface, and the solar matter torn off as a result of this was the material that later formed the planets. Under the action of the intruding star, the front part of the tidal wave should have developed a conical point from which matter would flow toward the intruder, forming a gaseous filament that would break up into a number of separate drops (Figure 5), thus giving rise to individual planets.

The collision theory of the origin of the planetary system held its ground for almost half a century, but, as time went by, it ran into more and more difficulties. The most im-

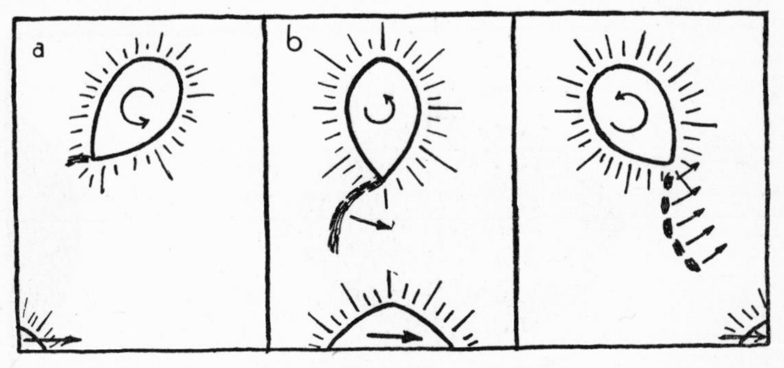

FIGURE 5
The Sun emits a gaseous filament, which is later broken into separate planets (tidal theory).

portant of these difficulties was the old Laplace objection to the original Buffon theory: the planets formed in a collision between two stars should describe elongated elliptical orbits, and not nearly circular orbits as they do in the solar system. The piling-up difficulties of the collision theory left the cosmogonists between two stools; on one hand, the ring formation hypothesis of Kant and Laplace did not seem to work because of Maxwell's argument; on the other hand, the rejuvenated collision hypothesis of Buffon didn't seem to do any better.

BACK TO KANT AND LAPLACE

The Gordian knot of the theories of planetary origins was finally cut by a young German physicist, Carl von Weizsäcker, in the fall of 1943. Using the new information collected by recent astrophysical research, he was able to show that all the old objections against the Kant-Laplace hypothesis can be easily removed, and that, proceeding along these lines, one can build a detailed theory of the origin of planets, explaining many important features of the planetary system that had not even been touched by any of the old theories.

Weizsäcker was able to accomplish this principally because during the two preceding decades astrophysicists had completely changed their minds about the chemical composition of matter in the universe. Before that time, the chemical elements forming the sun and all the other stars were generally believed to be present in those bodies in approximately the same proportions in which they occur in the Earth. Geochemical analysis teaches us that the body of the Earth is made up chiefly of oxygen (in the form of various oxides), silicon, iron, and smaller quantities of other heavier elements. Light gases such as hydrogen and helium (along with other so-called rare gases such as neon, argon, etc.) are present on the Earth in very small quantities.*

In the absence of any better evidence, astronomers had assumed that these gases were also very rare in the bodies of the sun and the other stars. However, more detailed

* Hydrogen is found on our planet mostly in its union with oxygen in water. But everybody knows that although water covers three-quarters of the Earth's surface the total water mass is very small compared with the mass of the entire body of the Earth.

theoretical study of stellar structure led the Danish astrophysicist B. Stromgren to the conclusion that such an assumption is quite incorrect, and that, in fact, at least 35 per cent of the material of our Sun must be pure hydrogen. Later this estimate was increased to more than 50 per cent, and it was also found that a considerable percentage of the other solar constituents is pure helium. Both the theoretical studies of the solar interior (which culminated in the important work of M. Schwartzchild), and the more elaborate spectroscopic analysis of its surface, led astrophysicists to a striking conclusion that the common chemical elements that form the body of the Earth constitute only about 1 per cent of the solar mass, the rest being almost evenly divided between hydrogen and helium, with a slight preponderance of the former. Apparently this analysis also fits the constitution of the other stars.

Further, it is now known that interstellar space is not quite empty, but is filled by a mixture of gas and fine dust with a mean density of about 1 milligramme of matter in 1,000,000 cubic miles of space. This diffuse, highly rarefied material apparently has the same chemical constitution as have the Sun and the other stars.

In spite of its incredibly low density the presence of this interstellar material can be easily proved, since it produces noticeable selective absorption of light from stars which are so distant that their light has to travel for hundreds of thousands of light-years through space before entering into our telescopes. The intensity and location of these "interstellar absorption lines" permit us to obtain good estimates of the density of that diffuse material and also to show that it consists almost exclusively of hydrogen and probably helium. In fact, the dust, formed by small particles (about 0.001 millimetre in diameter) of various "terrestrial" materials, constitutes not more than 1 per cent of its total mass.

To return to the basic idea of Weizsäcker's theory, we may say that this new knowledge concerning the chemical constitution of matter in the universe plays directly into the hand of the Kant-Laplace hypothesis. In fact, if the primordial gaseous envelope of the Sun was originally formed from such material, only a small portion of it, representing heavier terrestrial elements, could have been used to build our Earth and other planets. The rest of it, represented by noncondensible hydrogen and helium gases, must have been somehow removed, either by falling into the Sun or by being dispersed into surrounding interstellar space. Since the first possibility would result in much too rapid axial rotation of the Sun, we have to accept another alternative, namely, that the gaseous "excess material" was dispersed into space soon after the planets were formed from the "terrestrial" compound.

From these facts a new picture of the formation of the planetary system emerges. When the Sun was first formed by the condensation of interstellar matter, a large part of this matter, probably about a hundred times the present combined mass of the planets, remained on the outside, forming a giant rotating envelope. (The reason for such behaviour can easily be found in the differences between the rotational states of various interstellar gases which condensed into the primitive Sun.) This rapidly rotating envelope should be visualized as consisting of noncondensible gases (hydrogen, helium, and a smaller amount of other gases) and dust particles of various terrestrial materials (such as iron oxides, silicon compounds, water droplets and ice crystals) which were floating inside the gas and were carried along by its rotational motion. The formation of big lumps of "terrestrial" material, which we now call planets, must have taken place as the result of collisions between dust particles and their gradual aggregation into larger and larger bodies. Figure 6 shows the results of such collisions, which must have taken place at velocities comparable to those of meteorites.

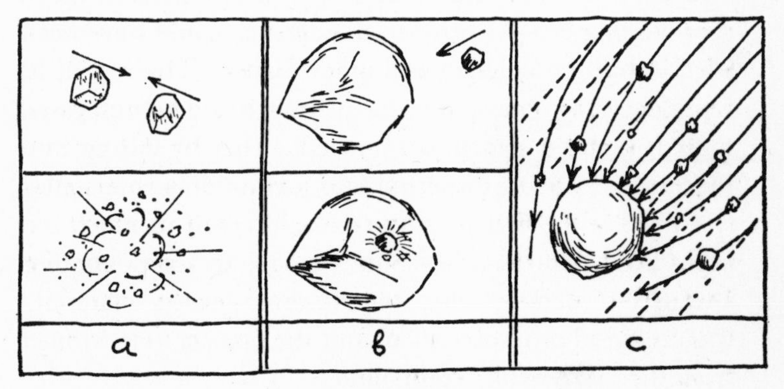

FIGURE 6
How the planets would have formed by accretion.

One must conclude, on the basis of logical reasoning, that at such velocities the collision of two particles of about equal mass would result in their mutual pulverization (Figure 6*a*), a process leading not to the growth of larger lumps of matter but to the destruction of the colliding particles. On the other hand, when a small particle collided with a much larger one (Figure 6*b*), it seems evident that the smaller one would bury itself in the body of the larger, thus forming a new, somewhat larger mass.

Obviously these two processes would result in the gradual disappearance of smaller particles and the aggregation of their material into larger bodies. In the later stages the process will be accelerated because the larger lumps of matter will attract gravitationally the smaller particles passing by and add them to their own growing bodies. This is illustrated in Figure 6*c*, which shows how, as the process continues, massive lumps of matter become increasingly effective in capturing smaller ones.

Weiszächer was able to show that the fine dust originally scattered through the entire region now occupied by the planetary system must have been aggregated into a few big lumps to form the planets, within a period of about 100,000,000 years.

As long as the planets were growing by the accretion of variously sized pieces of cosmic matter on their way around the Sun, the constant bombardment of their surfaces by fresh building material must have kept their bodies very hot. However, as soon as the supply of stellar dust, pebbles, and larger rocks was exhausted, thus stopping the process of growth, radiation into interstellar space must have rapidly cooled the outer layers of the newly formed celestial bodies, leading to the formation of a solid crust, which goes on getting thicker as slow internal cooling continues.

PLANETARY DISTANCE

The next important point which any theory of planetary origin must explain is the peculiar rule (known as the Titus-Bode rule) that governs the distances of different planets from the sun. The table on page 25 shows these distances for nine planets of the solar system, as well as for the belt of asteroids, which apparently results from an exceptional case in which separate pieces did not succeed

DISTANCE OF PLANETS FROM THE SUN

PLANET	DISTANCE FROM THE SUN (IN TERMS OF EARTH'S DISTANCE FROM THE SUN)	RATIO OF THE DISTANCE FROM THE SUN OF EACH PLANET TO THAT OF THE PLANET LISTED ABOVE IT
Mercury	0.387	
Venus	0.723	1.86
Earth	1.000	1.38
Mars	1.524	1.52
Asteroids	about 2.7	1.77
Jupiter	5.203	1.92
Saturn	9.539	1.83
Uranus	19.191	2.001
Neptune	30.07	1.56
Pluto	39.52	1.31

in collecting themselves into a single big lump. The figures in the last column are of especial interest. In spite of some variations, it is evident that none are very far from the numeral 2, which permits us to formulate the approximate rule: *the radius of each planetary orbit is roughly twice as large as that of the orbit nearest it in the direction of the Sun.*

It is interesting to notice that a similar rule holds also for the satellites of individual planets, a fact that can be demonstrated by the table on page 26, which gives the relative distances of the nine recognized satellites of Saturn.

As in the case of the planets themselves, there are quite large deviations (especially for Phoebe!), but again there is hardly any doubt that there is a definite trend toward the same type of regularity.

How can we explain the fact that the aggregation process

DISTANCE OF SATURN'S SATELLITES FROM THE PLANET

SATELLITE	DISTANCE FROM SATURN IN TERMS OF SATURN'S RADIUS	RATIO OF INCREASE IN TWO SUCCESSIVE DISTANCES
Mimas	3.11	
Enceladus	3.99	1.28
Tethys	4.94	1.24
Dione	6.33	1.28
Rhea	8.84	1.39
Titan	20.48	2.31
Hyperion	24.82	1.21
Japetus	59.68	2.40
Phoebe	216.8	3.63

that took place in the original dust cloud surrounding the Sun did not result in the first place in just one big planet, and the reason the several big lumps were formed at these particular distances from the sun?

To answer this question we have to undertake a somewhat more detailed survey of the motions that took place in the original dust cloud. We must remember first of all that every material body—whether it is a tiny dust particle, a small meteorite, or a big planet—that moves around the sun is bound, under the Newtonian law of attraction, to describe an elliptical orbit with the Sun at its focus. If the material forming the planets was formerly in the form of separate particles, say, 0.0001 centimetres in diameter,* there must have been some 10^{45} particles moving along elliptical orbits of all sorts of sizes and elongations. It is clear that in such heavy traffic numerous collisions must

* The approximate size of the dust particles forming the interstellar material.

have taken place between the individual particles, and that, as the result of such collisions, the motion of the entire swarm must have become to a certain extent organized. In fact, it is not difficult to understand that such collisions served either to pulverize the "traffic violators" or to force them to "detour" into less crowded "traffic lanes." What are the laws that would govern such organized or at least partially organized traffic?

To make the first approach to the problem, let us select a group of particles all of which had the same rotation period around the Sun. Some of these were moving along a circular orbit of a corresponding radius, whereas others were describing various more or less elongated elliptical orbits (Figure 7*a*). Let us now try to describe the motion of these various particles from the point of view of co-

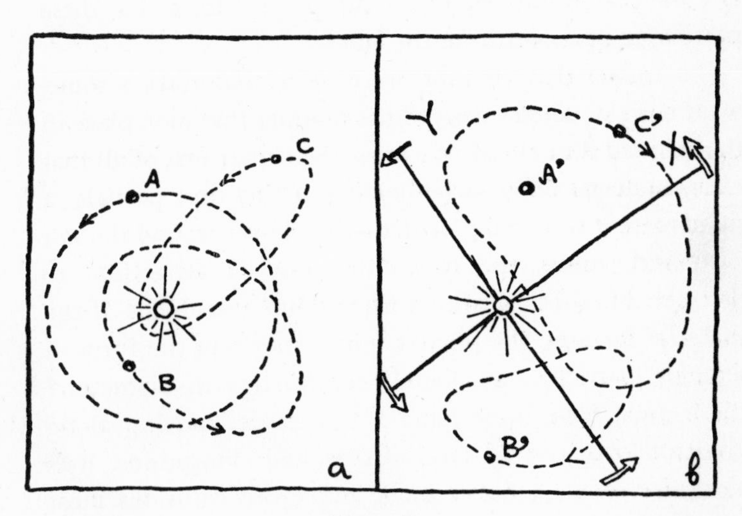

FIGURE 7
Circular and elliptic motion as viewed from (*a*) a resting co-ordinate system, and (*b*) a rotating one.

ordinate system *X–Y* rotating around the centre of the Sun with the same period as the particles (Figure 7*b*).

First of all, from the point of view of such a rotating coordinate system, the particle *A* that was moving along a circular orbit would appear to be completely at rest at a certain point *A′*. A particle *B* that was moving around the Sun following an elliptical trajectory comes closer to and farther away from the Sun, and its angular velocity around the centre is larger in the first case and smaller in the second; thus, it will sometimes run ahead of the uniformly rotating coordinate system *X–Y* and sometimes will lag behind. It is not difficult to see that, from the point of view of this system, the particle will be found to describe a closed bean-shaped trajectory marked *B′* in Figure 7*b*. Still another particle *C*, which was moving along a more elongated ellipse, will be seen in the system *X–Y* as describing a similar but somewhat larger bean-shaped trajectory *C′*.

It is clear now that, if we want to arrange the motion of the entire swarm of particles so that they never collide with one another, it must be done in such a way that the bean-shaped trajectories described by these particles in the uniformly rotating coordinate system *X–Y* do not intersect.

Remembering that the particles having common rotation periods around the Sun keep the same average distance from it, we find that the nonintersecting pattern of their trajectories in the system *X–Y* must look like a "bean-necklace" surrounding the Sun.

The aim of the preceding analysis, which may be a bit too hard on the reader but which represents in principle a fairly simple procedure, is to show the nonintersecting traffic pattern for individual groups of particles moving at the same mean distance from the Sun and possessing therefore the same period of rotation. Since among the original dust particles surrounding the primitive Sun we should expect to encounter all different mean distances, and correspondingly all different rotation periods, the actual situation must have been more complicated. Instead of just one "bean necklace" there must have been a large number of such "necklaces" rotating in respect to one another with various speeds. By careful analysis of the situation, Weizsäcker was able to show that for the stability of such a system it is necessary that each separate "necklace" should contain five separate whirlpool systems, so that the entire picture of motion must have looked very much like Figure 8. Such an arrangement would assure "safe traffic" within each individual ring, but since these rings rotated with different periods, there must have been "traffic accidents" where one ring touched another. The large number of mutual collisions taking place in these boundary regions between the particles belonging to one ring and those belonging to neighbouring rings must have been responsible for the aggregation process, and for the growth of larger and larger lumps of matter at these particular distances from the sun. Thus, through a gradual thinning process within each ring, and through the accumulation of matter at the boundary regions between them, the planets were finally formed.

This picture of the formation of the planetary system gives us a simple explanation of the rule governing the radii of planetary orbits. In fact, simple geometrical considerations show that in a pattern of the type shown in

Figure 8, the radii of successive boundary lines between the neighbouring rings form a simple geometrical progression, each being twice as large as the previous one. We also see

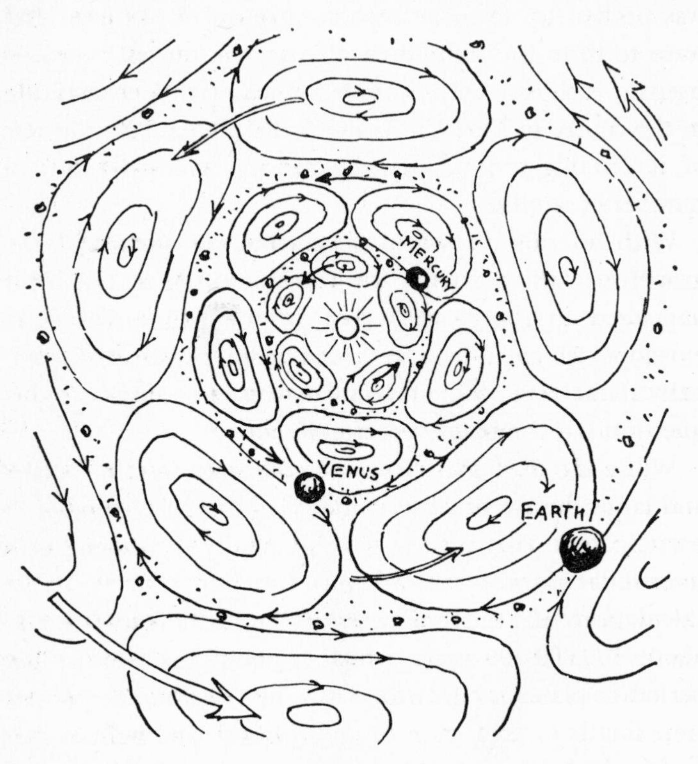

FIGURE 8
"Traffic lanes" of the dust in the original solar envelope.

why this rule cannot be expected to be quite exact. In fact, it is not the result of a strict law governing the motion of particles in the original dust cloud but must be considered rather as expressing a certain tendency in the otherwise irregular process of dust traffic.

The fact that the same rule also holds for the satellites of different planets of our system indicates that the process of satellite formation took place roughly along the same lines. When the original dust cloud surrounding the Sun was broken up into the separate groups of particles that were to form the individual planets, the process repeated itself in each case with most of the material concentrating in the centre to form the body of the planet, and the rest of it circling around and condensing gradually into a number of satellites.

With all this discussion of mutual collisions and the growth of dust particles, we have forgotten to tell what happened to the gaseous part of the primordial solar envelope, which, as may be remembered, constituted originally about 99 per cent of its entire mass. The answer to this question is a comparatively simple one.

While the dust particles were colliding, forming larger and larger lumps of matter, the gases that were unable to participate in that process were gradually dissipating into interstellar space. It can be shown by comparatively simple calculations that the time necessary for such dissipation was about 100,000,000 years, which is about the same as the period of planetary growth. Thus, by the time the planets were finally formed, most of the hydrogen and helium that had formed the original solar envelope must have escaped from the solar system, leaving only negligibly small traces which are known as the Zodiacal Light (Plate II B).

PLURALITY OF INHABITABLE WORLDS

One important consequence of the Weizsäcker theory lies in the conclusion that the formation of the planetary system was not an exceptional event, but one that must have taken place in the formation of practically all the stars. This statement stands in sharp contrast with the conclusions of the collision theory, which considered the process by which the planets were formed as very exceptional in cosmic history. In fact, the stellar collisions that were supposed to give rise to planetary systems were regarded as extremely rare events, and among 40,000,000,000 stars forming our stellar system of the Milky Way, only a few such collisions were believed to have taken place during several billion years of its existence.

If, as it appears now, each star possesses a system of planets, there must be, within our galaxy alone, millions of planets the physical conditions on which are almost identical with those on our Earth. And it would be at least strange if life—even in its highest forms—had failed to develop in these "inhabitable" worlds.

In fact, the simplest forms of life, such as different kinds of viruses, actually are merely rather complicated molecules composed mainly of carbon, hydrogen, oxygen, and nitrogen atoms. Since these elements must be present in sufficient abundance on the surface of any newly formed planet, we must believe that sooner or later after the formation of a solid crust and the precipitation of atmospheric vapors forming the extensive water reservoirs, a few molecules of such type must have appeared, owing to an accidental combination of the necessary atoms in the necessary order. To be sure, the complexity of living molecules makes the probability of their accidental formation extremely small, and we can compare it with the probability of putting together a jigsaw puzzle by simply shaking the separate pieces in their box with the hope that they will accidentally arrange themselves in the proper way. But on the other hand we must not forget that there were an immense number of atoms continuously colliding with one another, and also a lot of time in which to achieve the necessary result. The fact that life appeared on our Earth rather soon after the formation of the crust indicates that, improbable as it seems, the accidental formation of a complex organic molecule required probably only a few hundred million years. Once the simplest forms of life appeared on the surface of the newly formed planet, the process of organic reproduction, and the gradual process of evolution, would lead to the formation of more and more complicated forms of living organisms. There is no telling whether the evolution of life on different "inhabitable" planets takes the same track as it did on our Earth. The study of life in different worlds would contribute essentially to our understanding of the evolutionary process.

But whereas we may be able to study the forms of life that may have developed on Mars and Venus (the best "inhabitable" planets of the solar system) in the not too distant future by means of a trip to these planets by space ship, the question about the possible existence of life and the forms it may take in other stellar worlds hundreds and thousands of light-years away may remain forever an unsolvable problem of science.

ODD MEMBERS OF THE SOLAR SYSTEM

Apart from the regular planets and their satellites, the solar system possesses several "oddities" which may have originated some time after its formation. We have already mentioned the ring of asteroids which move in the gap between Mars and Jupiter where, according to the Titus-Bode rule and Weizsäcker's theory an extra planet should be found. Although most asteroids move in the region about halfway between Mars and Jupiter, some of them exceed these limits. On its closest approach to the Sun the asteroid Eros, for example, crosses the orbit of Mars and can be observed at a distance of only 22,260,000 kilometres from the Earth. On the other hand, Hidalgo, the most distant asteroid, reaches the point outside of the orbit of Jupiter. The largest asteroids, such as Ceres, Pallas, Juno, and Vesta, are several hundred miles in diameter, while the smallest visible ones are "mountains broken loose" no more than ten miles across. In spite of their comparatively large number, the combined mass of all the known asteroids is small compared with the Earth's, and, even allowing for smaller, as yet undiscovered members of this family, one comes to the conclusion that the total mass of the swarm is not much larger than one per cent of the Earth's.

The meteorites which fall on the surface of the Earth and are stored in our museums apparently belong to the same family as the asteroids, and their chemical analysis can tell us something about the origin of the asteroid ring. The studies in this direction indicate that material of meteorites must have crystallized under very high pressure, a conclusion which is also supported by the fact that small diamonds have been found in several iron meteorites. These findings strongly suggest that meteorites and presumably asteroids are the fragments of a large planet which was once moving between Mars and Jupiter, and not the condensations of the original material of the solar envelope which for some reason never formed a planet. But what exactly happened, and what hit this lost planet, smashing it into billions of pieces, will probably remain forever a mystery.

Another oddity in the solar system is the planet Pluto, discovered in 1930 on the basis of theoretical calculations. Pluto moves beyond the orbit of Neptune along a rather unusual orbit. While all planetary orbits are very nearly circles, and are only very slightly tilted in respect to the plane of ecliptics, Pluto's orbit is strongly elongated and its tilt is about 18 degrees. It is interesting to notice that while at its largest distance from the sun Pluto gets out into space much farther than Neptune, its closest approach to the sun is somewhat smaller than the radius of Neptune's orbit, so that two orbits actually intersect. From the direct observation of Pluto's diameter, astronomers concluded that its mass is only 3 per cent of that of the Earth, which would make it far the smallest member of the planetary family. All this leads to the conclusion that Pluto is probably not at all the original planet but a former satellite of Neptune which was kicked out into the solar orbit as the result of gravitational conflict with two other satellites of Neptune: Triton and Nereid. The orbits of these two remaining satellites bear the evidence of that battle which took place billions of years ago: Triton revolves around Neptune in the retrograde direction, while the orbit of Nereid is highly eccentric.

Beyond Pluto's orbit lies a wide region populated by comets which once in a while come close inside of the system of planets and develop brilliant tails under the action of the intensive solar radiation. The study of comets indicates that they are formed mostly from hydrogen compounds of carbon, nitrogen, and oxygen (methane, ammonia, and water), i.e., the substances which were forming the atmospheres of the planets during their formation and were later blown away by the radiation pressure of the sunlight. This completes our description of the main features of the solar system.

CHAPTER III

The Earth Bears a Daughter

OUR MOON IS "SOMETHING DIFFERENT"

IN Chapter II we saw that the birth of the planets' satellites probably took place in a manner similar to the birth of the planets themselves, that is, by the condensation of thin gaseous filaments extracted from the corresponding parent planets by the tidal forces of the Sun while the planets were still gaseous and their orbits still very much elongated. This origin accounts at once for the fact that the masses of the satellites are very small, compared with their parent bodies. But we have also mentioned that our Moon represents a striking exception among all other satellites, in that its mass is only eighty-one times smaller than the mass of the Earth (in all other cases the ratio of masses is of the order of several hundred thousands). It is highly unlikely that such a comparatively large mass of matter could have been formed from a thin gaseous filament, and we must look for a somewhat different explanation of the birth of our queen of night.

An instructive analysis of the unusual circumstances that were probably responsible for the birth of the Moon was given by the English astronomer Sir George H. Darwin, who was as much interested in the evolution of the world of planets as his celebrated father was in the evolution of the animal world. According to Darwin, the separation of the Moon from the parent body of the Earth took place during a comparatively late stage of evolution, when the Earth had already cooled off to a liquid state, while its surface may even have been covered with a thin, solid crust. We have seen that the filament is formed only when the body acted upon by tidal forces is in the gaseous state and consequently possesses a strong concentration of matter toward its centre. In the case of the liquefied Earth, the density must have been almost the same throughout its body because liquids are relatively incompressible,*

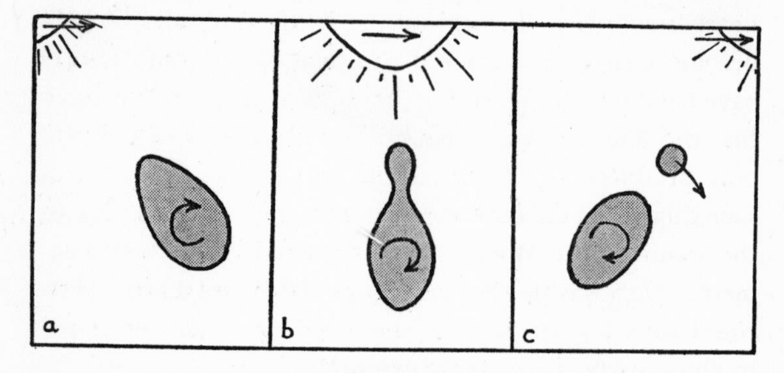

FIGURE 9
A liquid body subject to a strong tidal force forms a large bulge and then breaks up into two pieces of comparable size.

and the process of disruption by solar tidal forces must have taken a rather different form. In fact, Jeans, in his study of the equilibrium figures of rotating liquids, has shown that in this case a large bulge will be formed on the frontal part of the disturbed body instead of a conical point's ejecting a thin filament.

When the attraction exceeds a certain limit, this bulge separates from the main body and forms a liquid satellite containing an appreciable amount of the original mate-

* In the liquid state some increase of density toward the centre must take place because of the sinking of the heavier components in the mixture of elements forming the planet. But as this increase of central density amounts to no more than a factor of two, it does not affect our conclusion.

rial (Figure 9). This process is evidently exactly what we need to explain the birth of the Moon, but a somewhat more detailed study of the problem reveals that serious difficulties still confront us. During the early passages of our newborn Earth near the Sun, when its orbit was still greatly elongated and its distance from the Sun at its closest approach still small, the Earth most probably was yet in a gaseous state. On the other hand, when liquefaction finally took place, the orbit of the Earth must have already become nearly circular, and the tidal forces could hardly have been more efficient than they are at present. We know that the Sun, acting on the liquid envelope of our Earth, now produces an ocean tide of only twenty centimetres (one-quarter of the total observed tide, the rest being due to the action of the Moon) whereas a tide thousands of kilometres high was needed to disrupt the liquid Earth. How could such a gigantic tide have been raised on the Earth in those early stages of its evolution?

THE RESONANCE THEORY

Darwin's explanation of the origin of the giant tidal wave was essentially based on one magic word: *resonance*. The phenomenon of resonance must be very familiar to everyone who has ever pushed a boy sitting on a swing. If the intervals between successive pushes do not coincide with the period of the swing, they will sometimes help and sometimes hinder the motion, and the swing will remain almost at rest. But if one times the pushes to coincide exactly with the period of free oscillation of the swing, the amplitude will rapidly increase and, if there is little friction, soon reach very high values.

The danger of such resonance phenomena causes officers

to order a column of marching soldiers to break step while crossing a bridge, for the bridge might collapse if the "right, left, right, left" tempo should happen to coincide with the period of the bridge's oscillations. Likewise, in designing steam engines for ships it is very important to make sure that there is no resonance between the period of the engine and any free oscillation of the ship's hull. But, as we are dealing here with the oscillations of the liquid body of the Earth, the best example is probably that of a waiter hurrying with a cup of coffee. It is unfortunate for the diner-out that the oscillation period of the liquid in an average-sized cup almost coincides with the period of the steps of a rapidly moving man. The periodic impulses received by the coffee and increased by the resonance effect usually cause the coffee to splash over the edge of the cup into the saucer; such at least were the observations of the author in many quick-service restaurants.

Returning from coffee to the liquid Earth, we must conclude that extremely high tides could have risen on its surface if the period of the Sun's tidal forces ever coincided with the free oscillation of the Earth's body. It can be calculated that the period of free oscillation of a liquid sphere the size of our Earth is just about two hours. This period was only slightly higher when the material of the Moon formed a part of the Earth, thus increasing its total mass by 1.25 per cent and its radius by 0.4 per cent. On the other hand, the period of tides, which occur twice daily, is twelve hours at present, so that resonance in the body of the Earth is out of the question today. Darwin pointed out, however, that when the Moon was still an integral part of the Earth the rotation of the entire system about its axis must have been considerably faster.

It is not difficult to estimate this increased speed of rotation in an elementary way, by applying the law of the conservation of rotational momentum discussed in Chapter II. At present the Moon rotates around the Earth at a distance of about 60 times the Earth's radius and makes a complete revolution in about 28 days. When the matter comprising the Moon was part of the Earth, its average distance was evidently about half of the Earth's radius. More careful calculations, which also take into account the increase of density toward the centre of the Earth, give 0.55 of the Earth's radius as the exact value. Thus, at that time the distance of the Moon's material from the axis of rotation was $\frac{60}{0.55} = 110$ times shorter than it is now, and its linear velocity must have been 110 times larger, according to the law of conservation of rotational momentum, so that this matter made a complete revolution around the axis $(110)^2 = 12{,}100$ times faster than the Moon does now. For the period of revolution we get $\frac{28}{12{,}100}$ days, or only 3½ minutes. This is 400 times faster than the Earth itself rotates now, and, as the Moon and the Earth were a single body at the time, the whole must have been rotating at some intermediate speed. This average speed, in which the rotation of the Earth and the Moon participated in proportion to their respective masses, can be calculated from the simple formula: (average speed of rotation) = (the present speed of the Earth's rotation) $+ \frac{1}{81}$ (the speed of the Moon's rotation) $= (1 + \frac{400}{81})$ (the present speed of the Earth's rotation) = 6 (the present speed of the Earth's rotation). Thus the primitive

Earth-Moon body was rotating around its axis six times faster than the Earth does now, making a complete revolution in four hours. *The tides, which rise twice during each revolution, must have had a period of two hours, thus coinciding with the period of free oscillation of the whole body.*

This coincidence of the two periods, discovered by Sir George Darwin, must have led to a resonance-induced increase of the tidal waves in the liquid body of the young Earth, and it is only this rare "streak of luck" that enables us to enjoy the beauty of moonlight nights! Of course, the increase in the amplitude of the tides due to resonance must have taken some time, and it can be estimated from the theory of resonance that the tidal wave had to rise and fall at least two million times before the increase in amplitude necessary for the final rupture was attained. As the tides followed each other every two hours at that time, we conclude that *it took the Earth about 500 years to give birth to its ponderous baby.*

We can now reconstruct the whole picture of the Moon's birth: the Earth, which was condensed from the solar nebula along with other planets, for some reason or other failed to get a satellite in the ordinary way and remained childless, though most of the other planets had enjoyed large families of their own for a comparatively long time. The lonely gaseous body of the Earth rapidly cooled and shrank, and large drops of liquid material began to form in its interior, announcing the beginning of final liquefaction. When the whole Earth became liquid, and a thin, solid crust—the forerunner of advanced age—began to form on its surface, it was still childless. But here a miracle happened: the radius of the contracting Earth reached a value at which the period of the solar tides coincided with the period of free oscillation of the maturing planet's body.

This put new life into its body, and the tidal waves began to grow larger and larger with each rotation. In some 500 years (which is a very short time, of course, compared with the total life span of planets) the tidal bulge on the day side of the Earth became very large and unstable, and a giant liquid drop broke from the Earth's surface. From then on, the Earth had a satellite, a bigger and better satellite than any other of its sister planets.

If the Moon was formed from a big bulge on the surface of the Earth, some interesting conclusions can be drawn concerning the materials of which it consists. As we have mentioned, our Earth consists of a number of shells, with the heavier materials in the central regions and the lighter ones on the surface. Modern geophysics recognizes the existence of three major shells. The outer crust of the Earth consists of a layer of granite (with an average density 2.7 times that of water) extending to a depth of from 50 to 100 kilometres. This granite layer rests on a layer of heavier volcanic material, known as basalt, which is probably several thousand kilometres deep and reaches almost half-way to the centre of the Earth. Still farther down we find a molten core, consisting mostly of iron and other heavy metals. The presence of this metallic core, with a density of about 10 (probably even higher), is responsible for the fact that the mean density of the Earth, as estimated from its known total mass and volume, is about 5.5, that is, more than twice the density of the rocks found on its surface. This separation of materials is due to gravity, of course, and must have taken place when the

Earth was still entirely liquid, permitting easy circulation between the centre and the surface. Thus, when the big tidal bulge separated from the Earth, it probably took with it large quantities of molten granites and basalts, but only a very small amount, if any, of the heavy metals from the central regions. Consequently, we must expect that the mean density of the Moon should be considerably lower than that of the Earth and only slightly higher than the densities of granites and basalts. This expectation is splendidly confirmed by observations that give the value of 3.3 for the mean density of the Moon. Thus, in contrast to the Earth, *our Moon must be of stony structure throughout its entire body.*

HOW THE MOON ESCAPED

If the Moon is simply a giant lump of matter torn from the body of Mother Earth, how did it manage to get so far away from the place of its origin* and is it still receding? In fact, it is obvious that the Moon must have been revolving "almost within touch" of the Earth's surface immediately after the separation, and reached its present comparatively large distance owing to forces that were slowly pushing it away and causing it to move along an unwinding spiral orbit. These forces must undoubtedly arise in the gravitational interaction of two bodies, but who would ever imagine that gravitational attraction could push anything away? Nevertheless, it was shown by Darwin that the gravitational pull of the Earth caused (and still is causing) its satellite to move steadily farther and farther away through a rather complicated mechanism

* The present distance to the Moon is 384,000 kilometres, or 60 radii of the Earth.

of tidal action. In order to understand this process we must first study in some detail the effect produced by the Moon on the liquid envelope of the Earth, that is, the phenomenon of ocean tides. As we have seen, the phenomenon of tides is a result of the fact that the forces of lunar attraction are stronger on the frontal side of the Earth (i.e., the side turned toward the Moon) than on its posterior side. Owing to this difference in attraction, two tidal waves arise on opposite sides of the Earth and tend to follow in their motion the revolution of the Moon. But the Earth rotates faster than the Moon revolves around it, and therefore these two waves must travel around the surface of the Earth, completing a full revolution in about 24 hours and producing the well-known phenomenon of periodic high and low tides. In this motion the tidal waves meet with definite resistance in the form of continents and other irregularities on the Earth's surface, or, to put it more correctly, the tidal waves in the Earth's liquid envelope act as a brake upon the rotation of the solid body of the Earth.

Although the friction caused by tidal waves in their unceasing travel around the Earth's surface is rather small, it succeeds in slowing down the Earth's rotation around its axis by a minute amount, so that our day grows longer and longer. The detailed study of tides, to which we shall return later, leads us to conclude that *because of the lunar tides the length of the day must at present be increasing at the rate of one second in every 120,000 years.*

It would seem that such apparently negligible changes in the length of the day could not be noticed even by the most precise astronomical instruments. Fortunately, this is not so; the cumulative effect of such differences, even during the period of recorded history, would result in a total-discrepancy of the order of several hours.* When we compare the data of solar and lunar eclipses as recorded by Egyptian, Babylonian, and ancient Chinese astronomers with data calculated backward from present astronomical data on the assumption of constant length of day, we can actually observe the expected discrepancy and thus prove beyond doubt the retarding effect of ocean tides on the rotation of the Earth.

Applying the same rate of change to the much longer period of some five billion years (which have elapsed since the separation of the Moon), we find that the length of the day must have changed from its original value of 4 hours to the present 24-hour day.

The lengthening of the day produced by lunar tides certainly cannot remain without consequence to the motion of the Moon itself. We have already referred to the fact that, according to one of the fundamental laws of mechanics, the total rotational momentum of a mechanical system (in this case the Earth-Moon system) must always remain unchanged. Thus, if the Earth's rotation begins to slow down because of the action of the Moon, the Moon itself must gain in angular velocity. *This acceleration of the Moon's rotation must have forced it to recede steadily farther and farther away from the Earth and brought it to its present comparatively great distance.* Figure 10 illustrates the forces that brought this about.

* From the above rate we conclude that 4000 years ago the day was 1/30th of a second shorter, so that the average lengthening of the day between then and now is 1/60th of a second. As 4000 years contain 1,460,000 days, the total cumulative effect should have been $\frac{1,460,000}{60} =$ 24,000 seconds, or about seven hours. This is not much, of course, but exact astronomical observations luckily do exist for times so remote in the past.

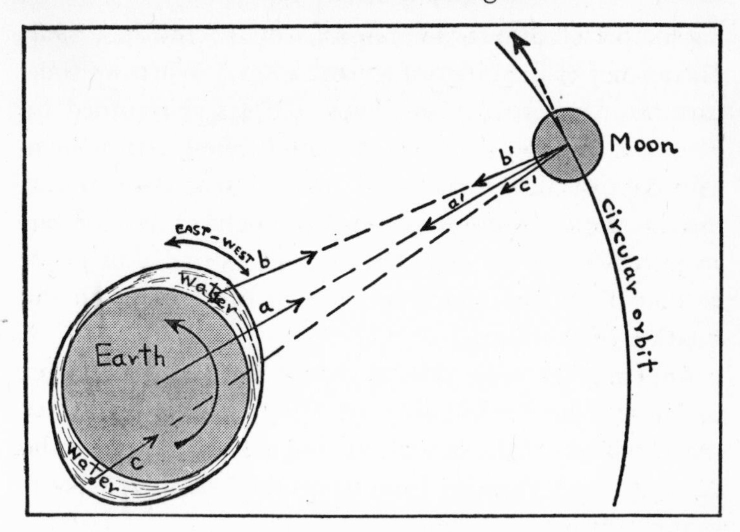

FIGURE 10
Forces that slow down the rotation of the Earth and push the Moon farther away.

Owing to the fact that the rotation of the Earth around its axis is much faster than the orbital rotation of the Moon (24 hours as against 28 days), the friction between the tidal wave and the ocean bottom drags the crests of the tidal waves in an eastward direction. Since the front tide crest is closer to the Moon than the rear crest, *the force* marked *b* in Figure 10, *pulling the Earth in the direction opposite to its rotation,* is larger than the force "*c*" acting on the rear crest, and the combined effect of these two forces *leads to the slowing down of the Earth's rotation.*

On the other hand, the two tide crests produce certain gravitational attraction forces on the Moon itself, the force b' being greater than the force c'. The combined effect of these two forces will be a drag along the Moon's orbit, *causing the acceleration of its rotation around the Earth.* Faster rotation results, however, in greater centrifugal force, and the Moon slowly recedes from the Earth, moving along a spiral orbit.

In the diagram the sizes of the tidal waves, as well as of those of the Earth and the Moon, are greatly exaggerated because of space limitations.

Exact calculations of this recession indicate that the time necessary to bring the Moon to its position would be about four billion years which is in reasonable agreement with other estimates of the age of the Earth.

As we have said, geological evidence indicates that the face of the Earth was rather different from its present state throughout a large portion of geological time, with large areas of the present continents covered by extensive shallow seas.* Since we know that the tides in the liquid envelope of the Earth meet the greatest resistance in shallow waters, we must conclude that the friction experienced by lunar tides was considerably higher during these stages of submergence and the Earth's rotation was being retarded at a correspondingly higher rate.

It may at first seem strange that minute changes in the distribution of land and water on the Earth's surface could have been of such great importance to the motion of the Moon, but it is an undisputable fact!

Further study of the effect of tides on lunar motion also reveals that our Moon, after receding to a distance several times greater than at present, will begin to approach the Earth again, come too close, and finally be shattered to bits. But we shall reserve discussion of this problem for the last chapter of this book, which is devoted to the future of planetary systems.

* More details about this "submerged" stage of the Earth's evolution will be found in Chapter VII.

TIDES ON THE MOON

During the epoch immediately following the separation of the Moon from the Earth, while both were still largely in a liquid state, giant tides must have also arisen on its surface as a result of the Earth's pull. The friction produced by these tides must have continuously retarded the rotation of the Moon about its own axis, and finally slowed it down to such an extent that in its travel around its orbit the Moon always presents only one-half of its surface to the Earth, a circumstance that sometimes gives rise to fantastic speculations about the mysterious "other side." The same phenomenon is known to be true of several other satellites, and also of the planet Mercury, which revolves around the Sun in such a way that one of its hemispheres has eternal day and the other eternal night.

Since tidal force is proportional to the mass of the disturbing body, earth-caused tides in the liquid Moon must have been eighty-one times higher than the lunar tides in our oceans; and if the distance between the Earth and the Moon was the same when the Moon was molten as it is now, lunar tides must have reached a height of about 50 metres. Detailed study of the shape of the Moon shows that it is in fact elongated in the direction of the Earth, but that *this elongation is about thirty times greater than should be expected for the tidal forces at the present distance of the Moon.* Since tidal forces decrease with the cube of the distance,* we must conclude that *the observed elongation corresponds to a time when the Moon was three times as close to us as it is now* (Figure 11). At that

* The force of gravity varies, according to Newton's law, as the inverse square of the distance, whereas the tidal force, representing the difference of gravitational attraction on two opposite sides of the body, involves the cube of the distance.

stage of development the body of the Moon evidently had become too rigid to permit further deformation; the tidal wave became "frozen" and remained unchanged ever after, although, because of the increased distance of the Moon, the forces responsible for the tides were considerably re-

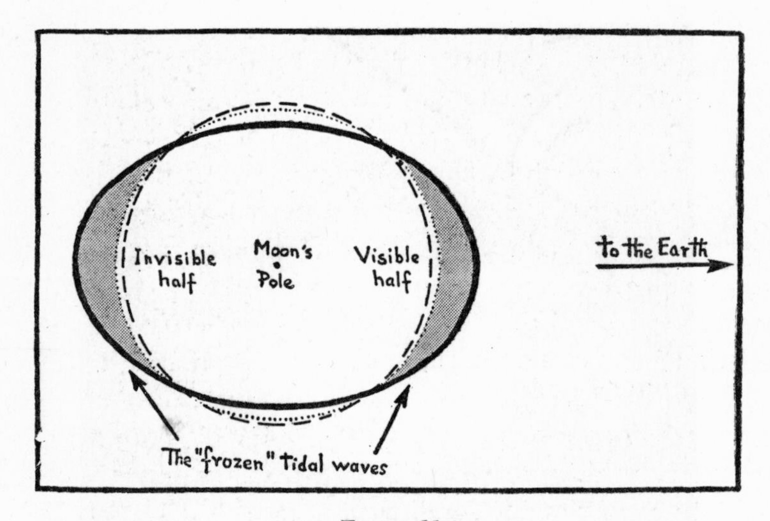

FIGURE 11
The figure of the Moon (drawn to an exaggerated scale) as seen from its pole. The broken line corresponds to the circular equator. The dotted line corresponds to the elongation that present tidal forces would produce. The solid line represents the actually observed elongation and corresponds to the time when the distance between the Moon and the Earth was three times as small as it is now.

duced. The presence of this "frozen tide" is evidence of the Moon's extremely high rigidity compared with our Earth, where deformations of the solid crust are constantly taking place even now (see Chapters V and VI).

It seems certain, therefore, that *the crust of the Moon is much thicker than that of the Earth, and our satellite is probably solid all the way to its centre.* This result can be easily understood, for the Moon must have cooled down considerably faster than our Earth because of its smaller mass.

It is well known that the Moon has no water, but if its surface were half covered by oceans, its geography would

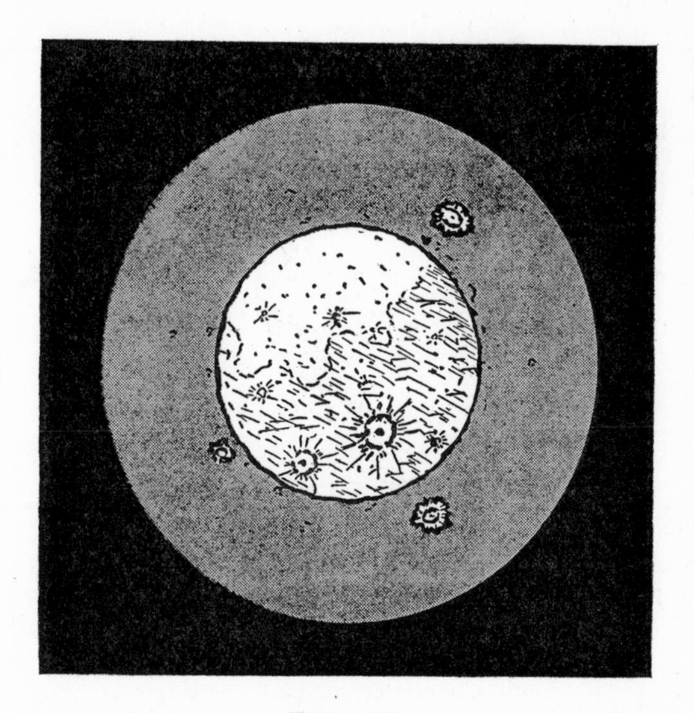

FIGURE 12
If there were water on the surface of the Moon, we could see something like this (*cf.* Plate III). The bright circle in the centre would be one of the two lunar continents.

represent a very peculiar sight—an almost circular continent, formed by the frozen tidal wave, right in the middle of the disk, with another antipodal continent of the same shape on the opposite side (Figure 12). The oceans would be rather shallow, reaching a maximum depth of some 750 metres at the visible rim of the Moon, while the continents would rise slowly from the shore line to a high point of about 750 metres above sea level at their mid-points. Since water has less reflective power than ordinary rock, we should see the brightly illuminated surface of the continent at the centre of the Moon surrounded by a considerably darker ring of water. Schoolboys, who rack their brains trying to remember all the seas, bays, peninsulas, and straits on the complicated face of our Earth, would just love such geography!

THE FACE OF THE MOON

The visible face of the Moon is rather different from that of our own planet. While the face of the Earth is wrinkled with numerous chains of mountains, the face of its satellite might be described as covered with numerous pimples. In fact, the most characteristic features of the Moon's stony face are the so-called lunar craters, which closely resemble the volcanic craters on the surface of the Earth, though on an immensely larger scale. The largest terrestrial craters do not exceed 10 or 12 kilometres in diameter, but the craters of the Moon are often 80 to 100 kilometres across and occasionally reach a diameter of more than 150 kilometres. A typical lunar crater is nearly circular, its circumference being formed by a ring of mountains sometimes rising as high as 7 kilometres above the surrounding plain.* The floor within the ring is comparatively flat, lying either below or above the outside plain; some of the craters are deep and some are filled

* The height of a lunar mountain is usually estimated by the length of the shadow it casts.

nearly to the brim. A group of peaks frequently rises in the middle of the crater, attaining about the same height as the mountains of the crater ring and sometimes exhibiting holes or craters in their summits as well. In many lunar regions craters are so thickly distributed that new craters overlap old ones, penetrating and partly destroying their structure; the whole picture represents a chaos of rocks more striking than in any similar formation on the Earth.

There has been much speculation concerning the origin of lunar craters. One hypothesis is that they are the results of the impact of heavy meteors on the surface of the Moon while still soft. The most probable explanation of these peculiar formations, however, seems to be the theory that they were produced by the gases liberated from the rocky matter of the Moon during the process of its solidification. It is reasonable to assume that the molten material of the Earth (and consequently that of the Moon) contained in solution a large fraction of the gases and vapours forming our atmosphere and the waters of the oceans. While solidification was taking place, these gases and water vapours steadily escaped through the viscous surface, raising giant bubbles which burst and left circular rims of elevated matter behind them.

"The earth hath bubbles, as the water has, and these are of them," was the explanation Banquo gave Macbeth for the sudden vanishing of witches. Whether or not this was the correct explanation of the strange phenomenon observed by the Shakespearian hero, it certainly hits the mark so far as the origin of lunar craters is concerned. The reader can easily visualize the process that took place on the surface of the Moon in the distant past by watching some pancakes fry and noticing the formation of bubbles and craters on their surfaces.

And now that our reader has returned from the kitchen with a refreshed mind and a pleasant feeling inside, he is ready to learn about other features of the Moon's surface. Aside from the craters, the most striking characteristic of the lunar surface is the so-called "maria" or "lunar seas," which were given this name by early observers, who imagined them to be large bodies of water. These maria actually are giant stony plains covering large areas of the Moon's surface. According to accepted views, they originated from giant eruptions of molten lava, which spread over the lower levels of the primordial surface of the Moon, burying thousands of older craters and forming extensive smooth surfaces of stone. The fact that but few new craters can be found on these broad plains of stone indicates that this vast eruption took place when the major process of the "bubble-crater" formation was virtually finished. The darker shade of the maria, compared with the surface covered by craters, is probably due to the poorer reflecting properties of lava or to the fact that the smooth stony surfaces of these plains scatter less light than the irregular rocky surfaces on the primary lunar crust.

Craters and maria are the most striking features of lunar topography, but there are a few long straight lines of moderately high cliffs, which are somewhat like the Earth's mountain chains. The rarity of such formations on the surface of the Moon, however, indicates that the contraction process, which most probably led to the rise of mountains on our planet (see Chapter VI), did not play an important role in the history of the Moon. There are also numerous straight clefts, half a mile or so wide and of unknown depth, running in some cases for hundreds of miles straight through the mountains and valleys and probably representing deep cracks in the crust of our satellite. Finally, there is the peculiar phenomenon of light-coloured "rays" diverging from some craters and several hundred miles long. The origin of these "rays," which are best visible during the full Moon, still remains unexplained.

It must be emphasized that, while erosion by water and air constantly changes and smooths down the Earth's landscape, the surface features of the Moon, untouched by these destructive agents (see Chapter IV), remain almost without change and thus present us with the complete history of their formation. There is no doubt that during the solidification of our own planet escaping gases formed numerous craters, of exactly the same character as those on the Moon. But all traces of these early formations have been obliterated by the action of water and air, and present mountain chains are of considerably later formation.*

THE SCAR OF RUPTURE

If the Moon had been separated from the Earth at a time when the latter was still completely molten, the liquid would have immediately covered the site of the rupture, and no more trace would have been left on the body of our planet than there is on the surface of a well from which a bucketful of water has been taken. But if at the time of rupture the Earth was already covered with solid crust, the newborn satellite must have carried away a large section of this rocky crust, leaving a clearly visible

* The only formation on the surface of the Earth that resembles the lunar craters is the famous "meteor crater" in Arizona, which, as its name indicates, is supposed to have been caused by the impact of a meteor comparatively recently.

scar. A glance at the map of the Earth's surface discloses such a scar in the deep basin of the Pacific Ocean, which now covers about one-third of the total surface of the Earth. It would, of course, be rather unwise to draw such a far-reaching conclusion merely from the vast area and roughly circular form of the Pacific, but geologists have discovered an additional fact that lends strong support to the hypothesis that the Pacific basin is

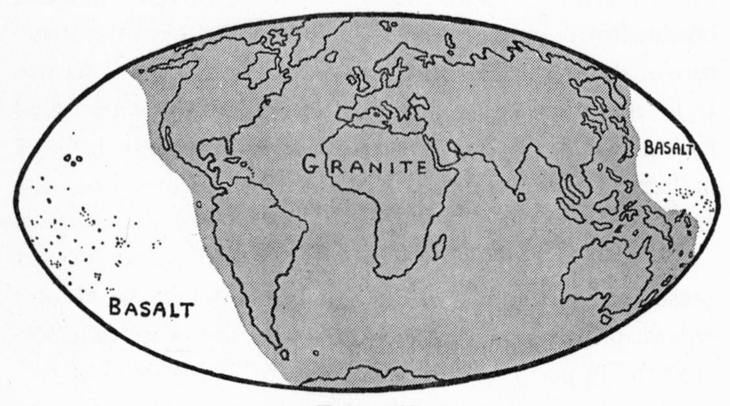

FIGURE 13
A schematic map of the world, showing the extent of the granite layer (shaded areas).

really the "hole" left in the Earth's crust by the separation of its satellite. We have already mentioned that the upper crust of the Earth is a layer of granite from 50 to 100 kilometres thick resting on a much thicker layer of heavier basalt. This is true of all the continents and also of parts of the Earth's crust that are submerged beneath the waters of the Atlantic, Indian, and Arctic oceans (Figure 13), where, however, the granite layer is considerably thinner. But the vast expanse of the Pacific is a striking exception *—not a single piece of granite has ever been found on any* *of the numerous islands scattered through that ocean.* There is hardly any doubt that *the floor of the Pacific is formed exclusively of basaltic rocks, as if some cosmic hand had removed the entire granite layer from all this vast area.* Besides, in contrast to the other oceans, the basin of the Pacific is surrounded by a ring of high mountain chains (Cordilleras, Kamchatka, the islands of Japan, and New Zealand) of pronounced volcanic activity, known as the "ring of fire." This indicates that this roughly circular border line is much more closely connected with the structure of the entire crust than the shore lines of other oceans. It is, therefore, quite likely that the area now occupied by the Pacific is the very place where the huge bulk of matter now forming the Moon was torn away from the Earth.

All this confirms the hypothesis that our planet already possessed a thin crust of solidified granite when the Moon's separation occurred. Since the part of the crust that covered the opposite side of the Earth probably cracked too, its various pieces may well have separated from one another, thus forming the basins of smaller oceans. In fact, we shall see later (Chapter VII) that, as Alfred Wegener first indicated, the shape of the shore lines of the Atlantic and Indian oceans strongly suggests that once upon a time the continents of Eurasia, the two Americas, Australia, and Antarctica formed a continuous continental block. The presence of granite at the bottoms of the oceans formed by enlargement of the cracks between the continents can be simply explained by the hypothesis that the lower part of the granite layer at that time still possessed a certain degree of viscosity (like taffy candy) and was stretched into a thinner layer covering the bottom of the slowly enlarging cracks. This conclusion can be supported, for example, by the fact that the volcanoes of past geologic epochs still ejected large masses of molten granite, whereas present volcanic eruptions consist entirely of molten basalt, which shows that the lower layers of granite had not yet solidified completely.

It is quite exciting to think that probably *all the familiar geographic features of the Earth are due entirely to the process of the birth of the Moon.* In fact, if our planet had been permitted to cool without any disturbances or catastrophic events at all, it would now certainly consist of regular concentric shells of different materials distributed in the order of their respective densities. In this case, the Earth's surface would originally have been quite smooth and completely covered with a universal ocean of constant depth. The subsequent cooling of the Earth's body would have resulted in the formation of long mountain chains rising above the ocean level much like the islands of Japan. The hypothetical present face of the Earth would then represent the rather unusual picture of an all-embracing ocean dotted with a large number of "Japans" of all kinds and descriptions (Figure 14). In order to produce the sort of Earth we actually have, with large and rather flat continental blocks of granite anchored into the deeper layer of heavier materials, some kind of rupture was absolutely necessary, and the separation of the Moon provides an excellent explanation of how it happened.

In the following chapters we shall return to the important question of how the Earth's surface originated. At this point we shall ask only whether traces of the rupture can also be found on the surface of the Earth's daughter. It is, of course, practically impossible to answer this question, at least until some adventurous geologist packs his hammers and drills and departs for the Moon in an interplanetary rocket ship—an event which may well take

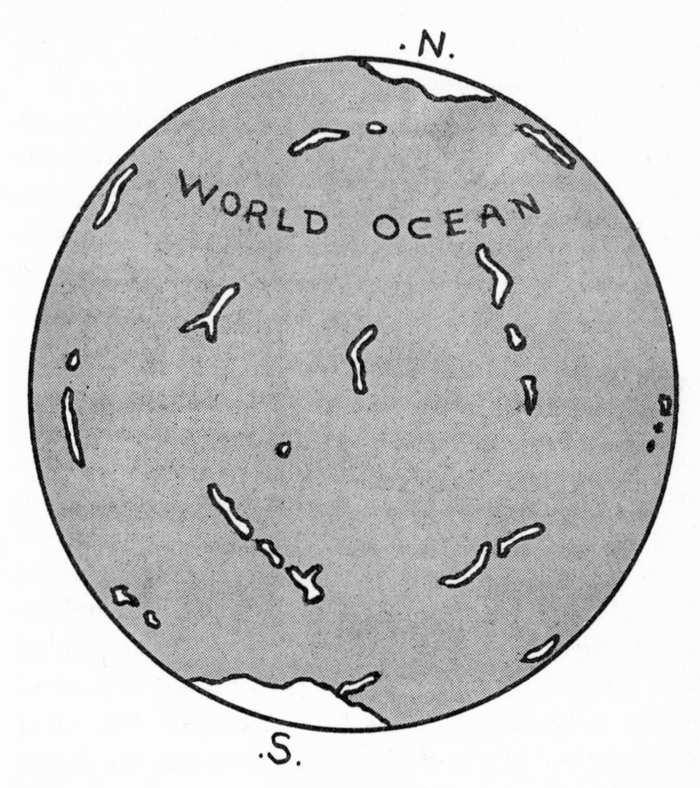

FIGURE 14
If the Earth had not given birth to the Moon, its surface would now look something like this.

place within the next few decades. We are restricted by the fact that the features of only half the moon's surface are directly visible to us. As a tentative hypothesis, one might suggest that the lunar maria (which we have assumed to be the result of violent eruptions of magmas during the Moon's past) originated at the same time as the basin of the Pacific Ocean, and that the lighter areas on the Moon represent pieces of the Earth's primeval crust that the Moon carried away with it. However attractive such a hypothesis seems, it is not very plausible, for the granite crust that once covered the area of the Pacific is five times as large as the entire surface of the Moon. Yet it is not impossible that different pieces of the primeval crust carried away by the Moon may have overlapped, leading to the formation of thicker and thinner layers of granite, the latter being subsequently inundated by molten material from the interior. But all this is, of course, bound to remain in the region of pure speculation for a long time to come.

CHAPTER IV

The Family of Planets

COMPARATIVE PLANETOLOGY

BEFORE getting down to the main subject of this book, our own planet, let us make a brief survey of the other members of the solar system and compare their physical properties with those of the Earth. This "comparative planetology," as it may be called, will help us to understand the characteristics of our own planet, much in the same way as comparative anatomy gives biologists a better understanding of the human organism by comparing it with those of mosquitoes and elephants.

We find that some of the planets, such as Mercury, are so small, compared with the Earth, that the attraction of gravity at their surfaces is too slight to hold down their atmospheres, which escaped completely into interplanetary space soon after their formation. Moreover, Mercury is so close to the Sun that its surface temperature must be unbearably hot—lead would melt on the side of Mercury that faces the Sun!

In the case of Jupiter, which is much farther away, the Sun cannot raise the surface temperature above —90° C. (—130° F.), even on the hottest "summer afternoon"; one would be able to throw snowballs all year round at the equator of this giant planet (provided, of course, one had enough strength to throw a snowball, which would be extremely heavy, owing to the strong gravitational attraction at Jupiter's surface). What is more, one would have to wear a gas mask while playing in the snow, because Jupiter's mass gives it a power of attraction great enough to hold a dense and extremely poisonous atmosphere.

FUGITIVE MOLECULES

To understand how planets lose their atmospheres, we must remember that the gaseous state of matter differs from the liquid and solid states in that gas molecules are free, incessantly darting back and forth in irregular zigzag paths and colliding with one another, while in liquids and solids the separate molecules are bound together by strong cohesive forces. Thus, if a gas is not surrounded on all sides by impenetrable walls, its molecules will rush off in all directions, and the gas will expand without limit into surrounding space.

In the case of our own atmosphere, which has no glass cover above it, of course, such unlimited expansion is hindered by the gravitational attraction of the Earth. The molecules of air that are moving upward against the force of gravity must soon lose their vertical velocity, much in the same way as an ordinary bullet shot into the sky. It is clear, however, that if we used some kind of "supergun" to give the bullet an initial velocity high enough to overcome the Earth's attraction, the bullet would escape into interplanetary space, never falling back to earth. From the known value of gravity at the surface of the Earth we can easily calculate that the "escape velocity" would have to be 11.2 kilometres per second, which can be achieved today by means of multistage rockets. The escape velocity for a given planet is independent of the projectile's mass; it is the same for a big-gun shell weighing a ton or more and for the minutest molecules of the air. The reason for this is that both the kinetic energy of the projectile and the gravitational forces acting upon it are proportional to its mass.

Thus, to determine whether the molecules of the atmosphere can escape from the Earth, we must know the velocities with which they move. Physics teaches us that molecular velocities increase with the temperature of the gas and are smaller for the molecules of the heavier elements. At the temperature at which water freezes, for example, the molecular velocities for hydrogen, helium, water vapour, nitrogen, oxygen, and carbon dioxide are 1.8, 1.3, 0.6, 0.5, 0.45, and 0.4 kilometres per second, respectively; at 100° C. (212° F.) these velocities are increased by 17 per cent, and at 500° C. (932° F.) they are increased by 68 per cent. Comparing these figures with the 11.2 kilometres per second required for escape from the Earth, the reader would be inclined to believe that none of these gases could ever take flight from our atmosphere.

This conclusion is not quite correct, however, because the molecular velocities given above are merely *average values,* that is to say, most of the molecules are moving at these speeds, while there always is a small proportion of slower and faster molecules. The relative number of these exceptionally fast or exceptionally slow molecules is given by the distribution law formulated by James Clerk-Maxwell. Using the Maxwell distribution law, we can calculate that the proportion of molecules possessing the velocity required to escape from the Earth is represented by a ridiculously small decimal fraction, with two hundred zeroes after the decimal point! But as there are always some molecules that can escape, they will do so, and their places will be taken by other molecules that formerly were moving more slowly. The percentage of such "fugitives" is considerably greater in the case of hydrogen molecules, which have a higher average velocity, while it is much lower for carbon dioxide molecules, whose average velocity is lower.

Thus we see that planetary atmospheres are gradually being "filtered" by this escape process, with large quantities of the heavier gases remaining long after the lighter gases are almost completely gone. As for "lost atmospheres," it is not a question of whether a given planet can lose its atmosphere (any planet can if given sufficient time!) but *whether the planet involved could have actually lost its atmosphere during the period of its existence.*

THE ATMOSPHERES OF PLANETS AND SATELLITES

Calculations have shown that the Earth is likely to have lost most of its atmospheric hydrogen and helium during the five billion years that have elapsed since its birth, whereas the heavier molecules of nitrogen, oxygen, water vapour, and carbon dioxide should have remained in large quantities. This explains why hydrogen is practically absent from our atmosphere, remaining on the Earth only in a combined form in water and certain other chemical compounds. It also explains why the inert gas helium, which forms practically no chemical compounds, is so rare on our planet, although astronomical evidence indicates it is abundant on the Sun, from which the Earth was originally formed.

Following the dictates of chivalry, we shall now take up Venus, which is the next smaller planet after the Earth and has an escape velocity of 10.7 kilometres per second, only slightly lower than that of the Earth. Accordingly, we must expect Venus to have an atmosphere only slightly more rarefied than our own, with large quantities of water. As Venus is nearer the Sun than we are and thus receives a correspondingly larger amount of solar radiation, much of this water must be present in the form of clouds that hide the beautiful face of the Goddess of Love and for ever obscure it from our eyes. This white veil of clouds, illuminated by the rays of the Sun, gives Venus an extremely high surface brightness and makes it the most brilliant of the planets (Plate VA).

As for Mars, which is the next smaller planet, possessing an escape velocity of only 5 kilometres per second, we must expect to find an atmosphere much more rarefied than ours, an expectation that agrees with the results of direct observation. Plate VIA shows two photographs of Mars, in which one half of the planet was photographed by ultraviolet light and the other by infrared. As ultraviolet rays are greatly scattered by the atmosphere, details of the planet's surface do not show at all in that half, the image actually representing a photograph of the Martian atmosphere itself. Comparing this half of the image with the other half, taken by infrared light and unaffected by the atmosphere, we are able to observe the extent of that atmosphere. Another proof of the existence of an atmosphere on Mars is the clouds that can sometimes be observed as small white specks on the surface of the planet (Plate VIB). These clouds, however, are considerably rarer than those over the Earth, from which we must conclude that water is rather scarce on the face of the bellicose planet. Although there are definite indications of the presence of water in liquid form on the surface of Mars, there are no big oceans comparable to ours, and the water is probably distributed in the form of extensive marshlands and shallow lakes.

Now we come to the smallest of all the planets, Mercury, whose mass is twenty-five times smaller than the Earth's and whose escape velocity is only 3.5 kilometres per second. No gas molecule could stay on so small a planet for more than a couple of centuries, and Mercury must have lost its atmosphere together with its water supply as soon as the gases were liberated from its cooling body.

The same situation prevails in even greater degree on the Moon (with an escape velocity of only 2.4 kilometres per second), as well as on all other satellites and all the asteroids. It is amusing to note that the force of gravity on the asteroid Eros is so small that a stone thrown upward by a good catapult would fly away and never return!

When we turn to the larger planets, Jupiter, Saturn, Uranus, and Neptune,* with escape velocities of 61, 37, 21, and 22 kilometres per second, respectively, we find an altogether different situation. The atmospheres of these giants among the planets not only retain oxygen, nitrogen, water vapour, and carbon dioxide, but also most of the hydrogen and helium that was present originally.

Since there is far more hydrogen than oxygen on the Sun, and consequently on these large planets as well, *all the oxygen is present in a combined form in water, with none left in the atmosphere, which consists chiefly of nitrogen, hydrogen, and helium.* We should also expect that since hydrogen is present in such abundance, it will

* On Pluto, which is but slightly larger than Mercury, we should also expect the entire atmosphere to be gone. Moreover, the temperature on its surface must be not far from absolute zero, −273.1° C. (−459.6° F.), owing to its distance from the Sun.

unite with carbon and nitrogen, forming the poisonous marsh gas, methane, and volatile compounds of ammonia, which will saturate this deadly atmosphere. Analysis of the sunlight reflected from these large planets does in fact show strong absorption lines due to these gases. On the other hand, spectroscopic analysis gives no indication of the presence of oxygen or carbon dioxide, without which life is quite impossible. Water vapour, which ought to be present in the atmosphere of these planets, is also absent. This deficiency, however, is easily explained by the fact that their surface temperatures are so low (owing to their great distance from the Sun) that all water is precipitated in the form of snow and ice.

Plates VII and VIII are photographs of Jupiter and Saturn. The markings on the disk are of atmospheric origin; no human eye has ever penetrated deep enough to see the solid crust of these planets.

CONDITIONS FOR LIFE ON THE PLANETS

When we discuss the possibility of life on other planets, we come to a delicate point, for we do not actually know what life is or what forms of life different from those on the Earth are possible. Life in any form is doubtless totally impossible at the temperature of molten rock (above 1000° C. or 1800° F.), or at absolute zero (—273.1° C. or —459.6° F.), at which all materials become quite rigid, but these are extremely wide limits. If we restrict ourselves to the ordinary forms of life found on the Earth, we can narrow these limits roughly to the temperature range in which water, the most essential constituent of organic structure, remains liquid. Some bacteria, of course, can stand boiling water with impunity for a time, while polar bears and Eskimos live in regions of perpetual frost. But in the first instance the death of the bacteria is only a question of time, and in the second we are dealing with highly developed organisms that keep themselves warm with furs and by a natural oxidation process within their bodies. From what we know of the evolution of life in the most elementary forms it can be concluded almost without doubt that life could not have originated or developed on the Earth if the oceans had for ever boiled or had been frozen solid.

We can, of course, conceive of entirely different types of living cells, in which silicon might take the place of carbon, thus permitting these cells to endure considerably higher temperatures. Likewise, we can imagine organisms that contain alcohol instead of water, and therefore would not be frozen stiff at glacial temperatures. Yet, if such forms of life are possible, it is hard to understand why no such "alcoholic" animals and plants are found in our own polar regions, and why the boiling waters of geysers are absolutely devoid of "silicon life." Hence it seems quite probable that the conditions under which life is possible anywhere in the universe do not in general differ greatly from those under which life is possible on our Earth. Accepting this tentative assumption, let us now investigate the conditions for life on the various planets of the solar system.

Beginning our survey with the large outer planets, we must admit that there is hardly a chance for life to exist on their giant bodies. These planets are far too cold, as we have seen, and life is also out of the question there because their poisonous atmospheres contain neither oxygen nor carbon dioxide nor moisture.

Among the smaller "inner" planets, Mercury not only lacks air and water, but is so close to the Sun that the temperature on its daylight side rises high enough to melt lead! We may recall that only one of Mercury's hemispheres ever sees daylight, because the action of solar tides long ago slowed down the rotation of this planet so that it always turns the same side toward the great central body. Eternal night reigns on the opposite side, where the temperature is far below the freezing point of water—nor is there any water to freeze. *No, life cannot exist on Mercury!*

This leaves us with only two other planets, Venus and Mars, our inner and outer neighbours. Both possess atmospheres comparable to our own, and there are definite indications that both possess an adequate amount of water.

As far as surface temperatures are concerned, Venus must be, in general, somewhat warmer than the Earth, and Mars somewhat cooler. The permanent layer of thick clouds that obscure the surface of Venus makes an estimate of the temperature on the ground below rather difficult, but there is no reason to expect that the temperature and humidity on Venus are much worse than, for example, in Washington, D.C., during a heat wave. On Venus's perpetually dark side the descending air currents must make the sky quite clear and the nights rather cool. These clear skies should offer us an opportunity to observe the surface structure of the planet, but unfortunately Venus—like every modest woman—removes her veils only under cover of darkness. Our inability to see the surface of Venus also makes it difficult to obtain any definite information about its rotation, though some recent observations indicate that a day on Venus must be as long as several weeks on the Earth. Since Venus's period of revolution around the Sun is 32 weeks, we may say that there actually is a succession of day and night. This picture is not so encouraging on the whole, but we may infer that *some sort of life, at least, is possible on Venus.*

Whether life really does exist on Venus is quite a different matter, which at first glance seems wholly unanswerable because no one has ever seen its surface. Certain information concerning the presence of living cells on Venus, however, can be obtained from a spectroscopic analysis of its atmosphere. *The presence of any type of vegetation on a planet's surface would necessarily lead to a noticeable concentration of oxygen in its atmosphere,* inasmuch as it is the main physiological function of plants to decompose the carbon dioxide of the air, consuming the carbon in the process of growth and liberating oxygen. As we shall see later, all the oxygen in the Earth's atmosphere is probably due to this work of plants; *if some catastrophe caused the grassy fields and forests to vanish from the face of the Earth, atmospheric oxygen would soon disappear,* being consumed in various oxidation processes. Spectroscopic analysis of the atmosphere of Venus fails to indicate free oxygen, though scientists would be able to detect as little as one-thousandth of the oxygen content of our own atmosphere. This leads us to conclude that *there is no extensive vegetation on the surface of Venus.* Without vegetation, animal life is scarcely possible, for, after all, animals cannot live simply by eating one another. Besides, there is no oxygen for them to breathe.

So it seems fairly certain that *life failed to develop on the surface of Venus for some reason or other,* despite relatively favourable conditions. This failure might be due to the thick layer of clouds on its daylight side, which might prevent the solar rays from penetrating to the surface in sufficient quantity to support the growth of plants.

THE ARID FACE OF MARS

Our outer neighbour Mars is the only planet whose surface can be observed in some detail, and hence far more is known about it than about all the other planets together. At its closest approach to the Earth, Mars is but 55,700,000 kilometres away, and its atmosphere is clear and transparent, with only occasional small clouds (Plate VIc). Spectroscopic analysis of its atmosphere discloses the presence of oxygen, carbon dioxide, and moisture, thus suggesting the existence of extensive vegetation and the possibility of animal life.

But because of its comparatively low escape velocity the atmosphere of Mars is now considerably more rarefied than ours, with an atmospheric pressure only one-tenth of that of the Earth. If man ever succeeds in reaching Mars, he will be subjected to the same atmospheric conditions that an airplane pilot would encounter at extremely great altitudes. Since its formation Mars has apparently also lost a considerable proportion of its water, and though the water has not disappeared completely, the climate of that planet is probably quite dry.

As seen through the telescope, Mars presents a rather smooth surface without noticeable mountain ranges like those on the Earth.* There are, however, permanent markings on the surface of Mars that suggest a definite type of landscape. About five-eighths of the surface is ruddy or

* Such mountains on the surface of Mars would be easily discernible by the long shadows they would cast during the planet's sunset.

orange-coloured, giving the planet the generally reddish tint that led the ancients to associate it with the God of War. The colouring of these areas always remains unchanged, and it is fairly certain that they are rocky or sandy expanses devoid of vegetation. The other three-eighths of the planet's surface consists of bluish-grey or greenish regions which were originally thought to be large basins of water much like our oceans and seas. Because of this assumption these regions still bear such names as Mare Sirenum and Sinus Margaritifer. But these darker areas are not water surfaces, for if they were, they would be much more uniform in colour and, what is much more important, they would reflect the rays of the Sun brilliantly under favourable conditions. The bluish and greenish tints suggest, on the other hand, the presence of vegetation, and this hypothesis receives strong support from observed seasonal changes in their colouring. In fact, the greenish colouring of these regions is most conspicuous during the spring period of the hemisphere in which they lie, steadily fading and turning yellowish brown as the winter period approaches. It is extremely difficult to conceive that anything but vegetation like that on our Earth would be able to produce all these effects, and, as the presence of free oxygen in Mars's atmosphere presupposes the existence of plants, we must conclude that *the darker regions are really plains covered with some kind of vegetation.*

Although no apparent areas of free water can be discovered on the surface of Mars, there is ample evidence of snow and ice, which form two brilliantly white caps at the poles of the planet (Plate VB). The seasonal changes of Mars are, of course, most noticeable at its polar caps. During the winter periods they extend almost half-way to the equator (in terrestrial terminology we should say that snow falls at the latitude of Boston), the rays of the Sun pushing them back to the poles again in the spring. The southern polar cap sometimes disappears completely during the hottest days of summer in the southern hemisphere. In Mars's northern hemisphere, which is the colder of the two (precisely the opposite of the state of affairs on the Earth*), the snow never disappears completely; it is merely reduced to a tiny white spot near the north pole. The disappearance of the polar caps on Mars is due not to its warmer climate (we know that it is colder than the Earth), but to the comparative rareness of water, which prevents the formation of a thick ice sheet. If snow formed only thin layers of ice at the Earth's poles, these layers would melt away under Sun even more quickly than the Martian polar caps.

Study of the growth and melting of polar caps offers a useful method of estimating the comparative heights of different landscape features on Mars. When the snow line retreats toward the poles in the spring, some white spots remain behind for a time, evidently indicating higher regions. Moreover, it is in these regions that snow first begins to fall with the approach of winter.† Since the "first snow" always appears on the reddish parts of the

* Owing to the ellipticity of the Earth's orbit, the Earth is closer to the Sun during the northern winter and farther from it during the northern summer. This makes winters in the Northern Hemisphere milder and summers cooler, while the Southern Hemisphere has colder winters and warmer summers. The colder winter in the Southern Hemisphere results in the formation of an antarctic polar ice cap that is larger than the one at the North Pole.

† Nowhere on the surface of Mars can we observe permanent ice formations like the eternal snow of mountain regions on the Earth. This is an additional proof of the absence of high mountains on Mars.

planet, we must conclude not only that they represent comparatively elevated regions, but that vegetation is concentrated at the lower levels. The difference in height between the upper and lower regions of Mars, however, is not very great; it is certainly much less than it would be on the Earth if the waters of the oceans should diffuse into interplanetary space, leaving the ocean floors exposed to the air and covered with vegetation.

We saw in Chapter III that the origin of the Earth's high continental blocks and deep ocean basins must be sought in the peculiar process of the Moon's birth. Since no such catastrophe occurred on Mars, which obtained its two satellites, Phobos and Deimos (Fear and Terror), in the ordinary manner, while still in a gaseous state, there is no reason to expect its surface to be as disrupted as that of our own planet. If there were more water on Mars, the planet would be entirely covered by oceans; it would appear to us as a smooth, evenly coloured sphere with occasional brilliant reflections of the Sun on its surface.

Temperatures on the surface of Mars, which seems to be the most comfortable place for life to exist beyond our Earth, are also of some interest. Measurements made with the bolometer, a highly sensitive instrument that records the amount of heat radiated by objects at vast distances, indicate that the noon temperature is only 10° C. (50° F.) or possibly slightly higher along the equator. Just after sunrise or before sunset the temperature must be well below the freezing point of water even in the equatorial regions, while the nights must be very cold.* The polar regions, of course, are much colder; at the ice caps the

* Occasionally small white specks are observed near the sunrise area of Mars; they disappear rapidly when the Sun rises higher over that area.

temperature is probably as low as −70° C. (−94° F.). Such a climate can hardly be called comfortable, but it is far from prohibitive for vegetable or even animal life.

Although vegetation definitely exists on Mars, proof or disproof of the existence of animal life is naturally much more difficult. Some forty-five years ago the romantic announcement of an American astronomer, Percival Lowell, caused great excitement in the scientific world and among the general public. Lowell claimed to have discovered proof, not only of the existence of animal life, but also of a high degree of culture among the "inhabitants" of Mars.

His claim was based upon the so-called "Martian canals," a geometrical network of perfectly straight, narrow, sharply defined lines on the surface of the planet that had been first reported by the Italian astronomer Giovanni Schiaparelli in 1877 and since described by several other observers (Plate VIc). If such "canals" actually existed, their geometrically perfect regularity could be explained only as the result of the activity of intelligent beings. And Lowell developed a bold and ingenious theory according to which these canals were constructed by Martians who, facing a scarcity of water, built a giant irrigation system in their desperate struggle for life on the dying planet. According to Lowell, the surface canals represented regions of parks and gardens stretching along these artificial waterways, which cross the barren, red-tinted deserts. He imagined that at the beginning of spring in one of the hemispheres, when the snow of one polar cap began to melt, the resulting water was artificially pumped along these

There is no doubt that these white specks are quite similar to the hoarfrost formed on the surface of the Earth during cold nights.

canals to supply the dry equatorial regions, and he even made an attempt to estimate the velocity of the water flow in the canals from the progressive changes in their colour.

These speculations are extremely exciting, and they would also be of great value if the "canals" actually existed. Unfortunately, however, they do not, as has been proved by observation made with superior telescopes and by advanced photographic methods. It seems that the network of canals reported by so many observers is simply an optical illusion arising from the tendency of the human eye to connect details by narrow lines forming a geometrical pattern whenever it looks at something near the limit of visibility. There are innumerable dark spots on the surface of Mars, but no straight lines or canals connecting them! And we still do not know whether or not there is animal life on Mars.

CHAPTER V

Journey to the Centre of the Earth

THE DEEPER THE HOTTER

LET us now return to the Earth and, disregarding the beauty of its surface landscape, start on a journey deep into the interior toward the centre of our globe. Yet, though we have very comfortable means of communication along the Earth's surface and can rise with Prof. Piccard into the extremely rarefied outer stratosphere, facilities for travelling downward are extremely poor. The deepest mines and wells of today hardly reach a depth of three kilometres, which is less than one-twentieth of one per cent of the total distance to the centre. Beyond this limit direct investigation is at present absolutely impossible.

But even with this comparatively small range of attainable depths, investigations reveal one extremely important fact: *the temperature of the rocks steadily increases as we dig deeper and deeper beneath the surface*. In deep mines the temperature always rises rather high, and in the world's deepest gold mine, the Robinson Deep (South Africa), for example, the walls are so hot that a half-million-dollar air-conditioning plant had to be installed to prevent the miners from being roasted alive. The most comprehensive data about the temperature distribution under the surface of the Earth are obtained from deep well-borings carried on in several thousand different localities all over the surface of the globe. Measurements in such wells show that *temperature increase with depth is quite a general phenomenon* and is practically independent of the geographic site of the observation station. Close to the surface there are always some deviations from uniformity because

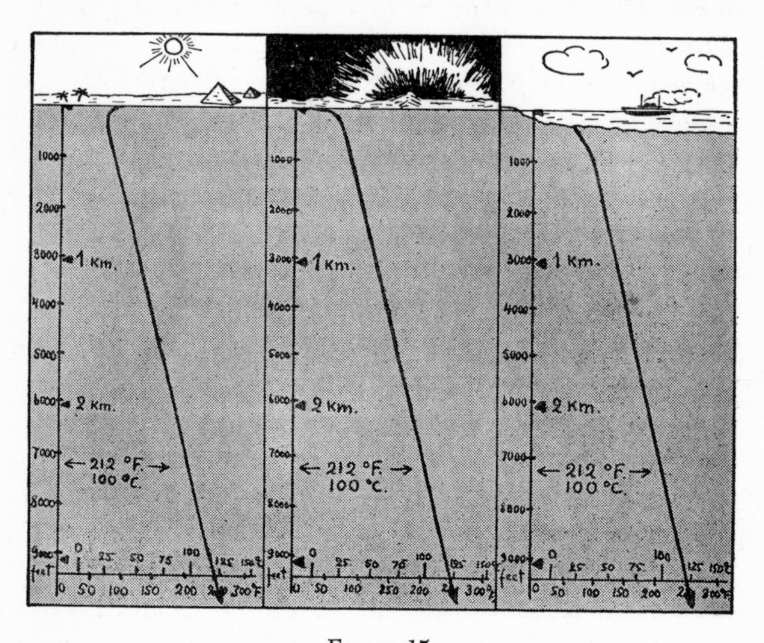

FIGURE 15

The increase of temperature at great depths does not depend upon conditions on the surface. At a depth of about 7200 feet the boiling point of water is reached.

of the prevailing climatic conditions, and rocks situated only a few hundred feet under the polar tundras are naturally somewhat colder than those under the Sahara Desert. Measurements made in wells bored through the ocean floor (not far from the shore, of course) also indicate that the temperature of rocks deep under the water surface is lower than those at the same depth under the continents. All these differences, however, are limited to a comparatively thin outer layer of the crust, and at greater depths the surfaces of equal temperatures run closely parallel to the surface of the globe. Figure 15, which gives the observed temperature changes in the accessible outer layer of the crust, shows that *the increase of temperature is remarkably steady there, amounting to about 30° C. per kilometre of depth (or 16° F. per thousand feet).*

Since the average temperature of the Earth's surface is about 20° C. (68° F.), *the temperature of rocks rises to the boiling point of water at a depth of only two and a half kilometres.* If water from the surface of the Earth, leaking through occasional cracks in the crust, reaches this depth, it begins to boil and is ejected by vapour pressure in the form of the magnificent hot geysers so familiar to visitors to Yellowstone National Park (Plate IX).

If the rise of temperature continues at the same rate through the first few dozen kilometres beyond the explored region (and there are no apparent reasons why it should not*), *the temperature of molten rocks (i.e., between 1200° and 1800° C. or 2200° and 3300° F.) must be reached at a depth of about 50 kilometres below the surface.* There seems to be no doubt that the molten lava that is ejected by the numerous volcanoes on the surface of the Earth (Plate X) originates at about the same depth. In fact, measurements of lava temperature inside the volcanic craters always yield the value of about 1200° C. (2200° F.), corresponding to a depth of about 50 kilometres. Volcanic eruptions, which long before the foundation of scientific geophysics led the ancients to the hypothesis that "Hell" is situated somewhere under their feet, give us the best proof

* We shall see in Chapter VI that deviations from the linear temperature increase can be expected only at greater depths.

of the thinness of the solid crust upon which we base all our life.

SOLIDS THAT FLOW AND LIQUIDS THAT CRACK

It seems at first sight that this evidence leaves no room for any doubt that *some 50 kilometres under our feet the rocks constituting the body of the Earth must be in a completely molten state and resemble ordinary fluids in all their properties.* And one may therefore be very much surprised to learn of another set of observational data definitely indicating that *the material of the Earth possesses all the properties of the ordinary elastic solid down to a depth of at least 3000 kilometres (i.e., half the distance to the centre).* In fact, we shall see later in this chapter that the observed deformations of the Earth's body under the action of the tidal forces of the Moon, as well as the earthquake waves propagated through the deep interior of our planet, *force us to consider the material of the Earth to be almost as elastic as a good steel spring.*

Is this really an unanswerable contradiction of facts, or can these two apparently directly opposite conclusions be reconciled in some way? *Can matter be fluid and elastic at the same time?* Of course, nobody would ever dream of making a watch spring of liquid water or of pouring an iron bar from a glass, but, strange as it may seem, there are many substances that unite in themselves these two seemingly contradictory properties: being a solid and a liquid at the same time! Let us take, for example, a stick of ordinary sealing wax and hit it with a hammer. The stick will, of course, break into many pieces, as if it were made of clay or glass. But if we put another stick of sealing wax in a jar and forget about it for a couple of years, we shall find that the sealing wax had spread all over the jar, filling it as if it were a liquid. In the same way, a coin placed on a seemingly solid surface of tar will sink through it if given enough time, while a piece of cork will move upward through the "solid" tar as if through the water. Another famous example is shoemaker's wax, which is apparently so rigid that it can be used for tuning forks. If, however, a musician using such a fork leaves it lying somewhere on the shelf for a long time, he will find to his very great surprise that his tuning fork has spread all over the shelf as if it were made of honey.*

From the strictly physical point of view, substances such as tar and various waxes must be considered as actually liquid bodies, and their apparent "solid" properties must be ascribed to their extremely high viscosity. They will certainly crack under the action of strong instantaneous forces, which try to change their shape much too fast, but they will flow under the action of weaker forces operating during sufficiently long periods of time.

The difference between these hyperviscous solid-looking substances and real solids, which would never flow, lies in their internal molecular structure. In real solids the molecules are arranged in a regular pattern, forming a so-called crystal lattice,† whereas the molecules of ordinary, as well as hyperviscous, liquids are distributed in complete dis-

* Ordinary window glass also belongs to this class of "liquid solids," although its "fluidity" is apparently much less than in the examples discussed above. Old glassware dating back to the first Egyptian Pharaohs has not noticeably changed its form during the thousands of years since it was fabricated; but the fluidity of glass must be expected from its non-crystalline structure, as we shall explain later.

† Although all solid bodies possess crystalline structure, in many of them the separate crystals are so small and so well moulded together that the fact can be proved only by microscopic investigations. This class of microcrystalline solids includes, for example, all ordinary metals.

order. In crystalline substances any dislocation of the molecules will give rise to forces tending to bring them back to their original position in the lattice, whereas in liquids the molecules will "slide" relative to one another, and their motion will be hampered only by the "frictional" forces between them. If these frictional forces are sufficiently large, the group of molecules will be able to change its form only very slowly and will simply break down at any attempt to deform it faster. The ability of molecules to "slide" depends, of course, on their nature, as well as on the degree of their compactness produced by outside pressure. At ordinary atmospheric pressure the molecules of most substances will "slide" rather easily as soon as thermal motion dislocates them from their original position in the crystal lattice, and only in very few cases, such as tar or wax, will the frictional forces be of any importance. But the very high pressures existing in the interior of the Earth,* the "squeezing" of the molecules forming the rocks will be so large that even above the melting point their fluidity will be extremely small.

This enables us to understand why, at great depths beneath the surface of the Earth, *rocks can react as perfectly elastic material to such comparatively rapidly changing forces as those originating in earthquake waves,† in spite of the fact that they are actually molten and would flow if given a long enough time to do so.*

The fluidity of matter at great depths, however, becomes apparent as soon as an occasional crack occurs in

* At a depth of 50 kilometres the pressure due to the weight of the rocks lying above is about 20,000 atmospheres.

† The tidal forces, changing in direction every six hours, can, of course, also be considered rapidly changing forces in respect to substances of such high viscosity.

the solid outer crust of the Earth. The hot plastic matter of the depths will be squeezed into this crack by the tre-

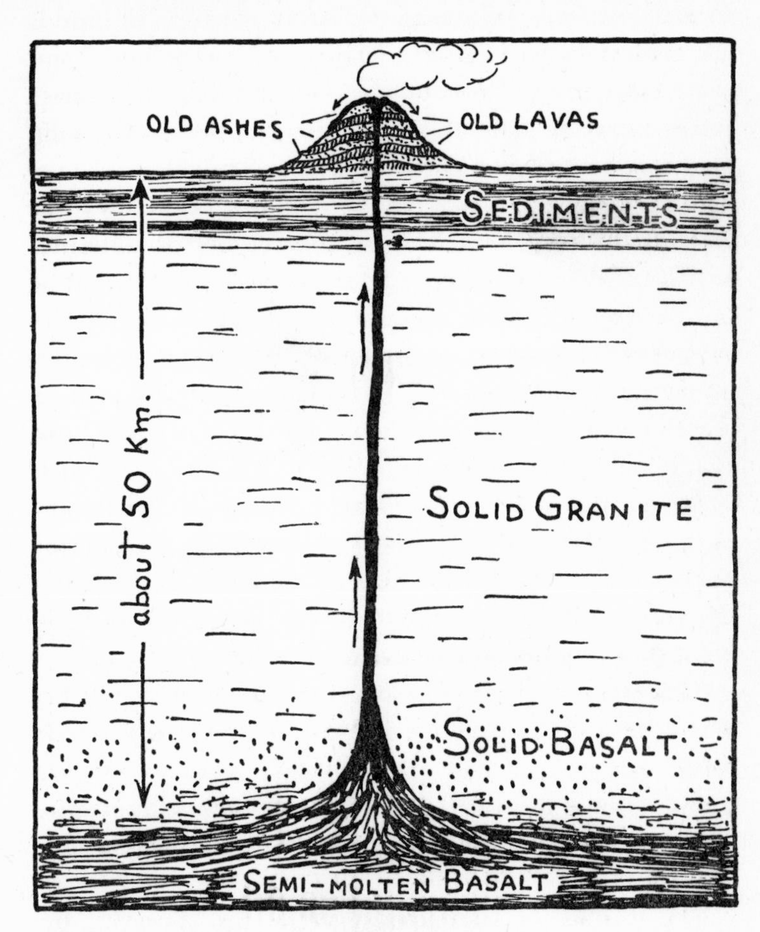

FIGURE 16
Schematic diagram of a volcanic eruption.

mendous pressures existing there, and will begin to move slowly upward to the surface. Coming closer and closer to the surface of the Earth, this molten matter enters the region of lower pressures, and its molecules gradually "loosen up." The molten substance slowly regains its mobility and comes out of volcanic craters in the familiar form of red-hot liquid lava (Figure 16).

It is, of course, not necessary that the crack in the solid crust extend all the way from the region of molten rocks to the surface of the Earth. There seem to be many instances where the molten matter stops before reaching the surface and spreads out horizontally, forming the nests of igneous material known in geology as "laccoliths." Such formations are often exposed on the surface if subsequent erosion has removed the layers of rock above them.

FLOATING CONTINENTS

It was stated in Chapter III that a considerable portion of the Earth's original granite crust had been torn away during the birth of the Moon to form the body of its satellite. The giant fragments of the remaining primeval crust, which were floating on the molten surface of the heavier basalt immediately after the catastrophe of the Moon's birth, now constitute the continental massifs, whereas the solidified outer layers of the exposed basalt (covered, with the exception of the Pacific basin, by a very thin granite layer) form the bottoms of the oceanic basins. The continental masses then floated in the ocean of molten basalt much as icebergs now float on the water surface of the ocean today.

To support the parts of the continents that protruded above the molten surface the continents must have been submerged, deep enough for the weight of the displaced liquid to equal the total weight of the floating body (Archimedes' law). From the relative densities of granite and basalt rocks (2.65 and 2.85, if water is taken as unity) it is easy to calculate that only one-thirteenth of the total thickness of the granite blocks protruded above the level of the liquid basalt.* After the outer layer of basalt solidified, and the continents became anchored in the new solid crust, their elevation above the basalt surface must have remained essentially unchanged so long as the newly formed ocean basins remained empty. As soon as the temperature of the crust fell below the boiling point of water, however, the rains falling from the skies began to fill these basins with their present water content. The additional weight of water pressed the bottoms down, and, since the comparatively thin solid crust of the Earth was unable to support this weight, certain deformations must inevitably have taken place. The ocean bottoms slowly sank still lower, while the continental blocks were compressed and pushed upward. It is not difficult to calculate that, with the waters filling the ocean basins almost to the brim as they do now,† the elevation of continental massifs above the basalt surface of the ocean bottoms must be about one-ninth of their total thickness. As the present average elevation of the continental surfaces above the ocean bottom is about 5 kilometres (4.25 km. + 0.75 km.), we must conclude that *the thickness of the granite massifs is about 45 kilometres.* This is in good agreement with the fact that the volcanic lavas coming apparently from a depth of about 50 kilometres consist entirely of basaltic material,

* We find from Archimedes' law that the protruding portion of a float must equal the density difference divided by the density of the liquid. Using the values given above we obtain for the protruding fraction:

$$\frac{2.85 - 2.65}{2.65} = \frac{1}{13}$$

† The average depth of the oceans is 4.25 kilometres, whereas the average elevation of land above sea level is only 0.75 kilometre.

whereas the volcanic eruptions of the past, which must have taken place at the time when the solid crust was somewhat thinner than it is now, were still ejecting large masses of molten granite. At the present stage of the cooling of our planet the solidification of the crust under the continents has progressed only very little beyond the demarcation line between the granite and basalt shells. *We*

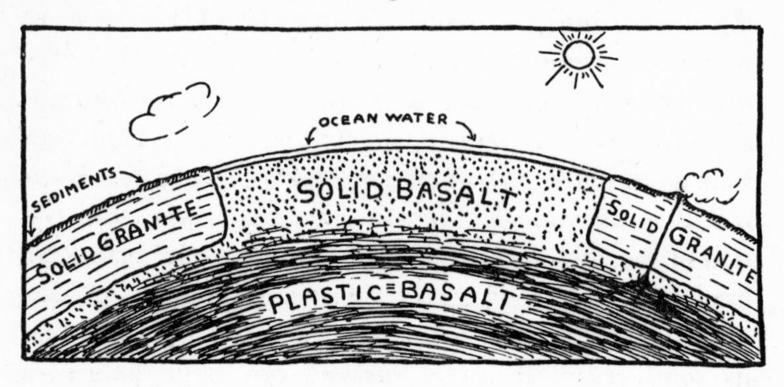

FIGURE 17
Structure of the Earth's solid crust.

must think of the solid crust as composed of separate pieces of two entirely different types of rocks, strongly soldered together and floating on the underlying layers of plastic material (Figure 17).

This adjustment of the Earth's crust under the action of the changing mass distribution on its surface plays a very important role in the evolution of the face of our planet and is known under the name of *isostasy*. As we shall see later, isostatic adjustments were important during the glacial periods, when the thick sheets of ice covered much of North America and Europe. The weight of the ice sheets caused the northern regions of these continents to sink deeper into the plastic layer underneath.

At the present time, when most of the ice is gone, the depressed parts of the continents are still slowly rising toward their pre-Ice Age positions, and we can notice a slow regression of the seas as, for example, along the shore lines of the Scandinavian Peninsula. We shall also see in Chapter VI that the crust bends in under the weight of great mountains and forms giant granite bulges protruding inward into the molten basalt. The phenomenon of isostatic adjustment reminds us once more that only a very thin layer of solid rock separates us from the interior regions, which are still in almost the same state as they were at the birth of our planet. In this respect the Earth is still much younger—not in years but in the preservation of the "fire of youth"—than the Moon. In fact, as we have seen, the Moon, being considerably smaller in size, must by now be solidified to a much larger degree, so that its solid crust can easily support two large bulges of "frozen tide" rising on opposite sides.

THE TIDES IN ROCKS

We have often mentioned the phenomenon of tides and, in particular, the importance of tidal forces in the history of our globe. It will be remembered that the tidal action of the Sun on the primeval liquid Earth, which, increased by resonance, resulted in the formation of the Moon itself, causes the periodic rise and fall of the oceans and slows down the rotation of the Earth.

But the effect of tidal forces is, of course, not confined to the periodic disturbances of the liquid envelope of our planet alone; the Earth's rocky body itself is being periodically pushed and pulled by the uneven attraction acting on its opposite flanks. We have already seen that the matter of the Earth's interior exhibits plastic properties only in response to forces persistently acting in the same direction over very long periods of time. *Since the tidal forces change their direction every six hours, we must conclude that in response to these forces the body of the Earth must behave as a perfectly elastic sphere.* Similarly, a ball of sealing wax will bounce if dropped on the floor from a certain height, but will flow under its own weight if left on the floor for a long enough time. Since the body of the Earth is certainly less deformable than its liquid envelope, the "tides in rocks" must be smaller than the tides in the oceans, and the rise and fall of the water level that we observe at the seashore must result from the difference between the heights of the two tides. Although we can easily measure this difference, the determination of the separate heights of the two tides is very difficult. In fact, since the tidal deformations of the Earth result in the periodic rise and fall of the entire surface surrounding the observer, the tides in rocks cannot be noticed by an observer on the ground, just as the ocean tides cannot be observed from a boat on the open ocean. One way to estimate the height of the body tides in the Earth would be to calculate the expected height of oceanic tides on the basis of Newton's law and to compare this value with the observed relative elevations of the ocean and land levels. Unfortunately, the theoretical calculation of the ocean tides, which would be very simple if the Earth were a smooth, regular sphere, becomes impossibly difficult because we must take into account all the irregularities of the ocean shores and the varying depths of the ocean basins.

This difficulty was solved in a very ingenious way by the

American physicist Albert A. Michelson, who proposed to study the "microtides" raised by solar and lunar attraction in comparatively small bodies of water. His apparatus consisted of a carefully levelled iron pipe, about 150 metres long, which was half filled with water (Figure 18). Under the action of the gravity forces due to the Sun and the Moon, the water surface in this pipe behaves exactly in the same way as the water in the oceans, periodically changing its inclination to a fixed direction in space.

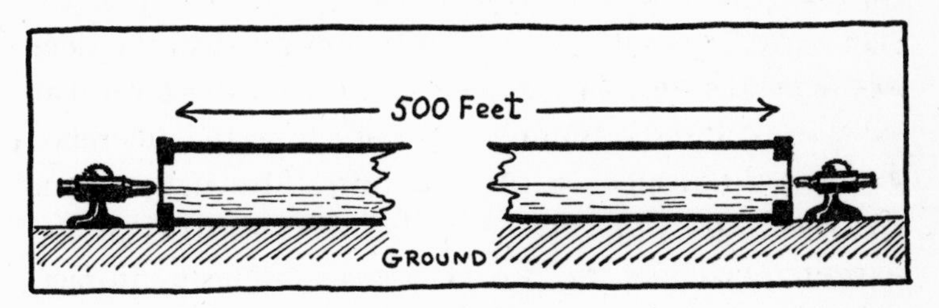

FIGURE 18
Michelson's apparatus for the study of tides under laboratory conditions.

Since this *"Michelson's ocean"* has considerably smaller linear dimensions than, let us say, the Pacific (150 metres as against 16,000 kilometres), the same inclination of the surface will cause only very small vertical displacements of the water level at the opposite ends of the pipe, so small in fact that they cannot be noticed with the naked eye. Using a microscope, however, Michelson was able to observe these small variations of the water level, which amounted to only *0.0004* centimetre at their maximum. In spite of the small size of these "microtides," he was able to observe all the phenomena familiar on a large scale in the ocean basins of our planet, such as the exceptionally high tides during new moon periods.*

* These high tides are due to the fact that during these periods the

Comparing the observed height of the tides in his "micro-ocean" with the theoretical values, which can be easily calculated for this simple case, Michelson noticed that they account for only 69 per cent of the expected effect. *The remaining 31 per cent was evidently compensated for by the tidal dislocation of the Earth's solid surface* on which Michelson's tube was installed. Thus he came to the conclusion that *the observed oceanic tides must represent only 69 per cent of the total rise of waters,* and that, since the tides in open oceans are about 75 centimetres (2½ feet) high,* *the total rise of water must be about 110 centimetres.*

The remaining 35 centimetres of this total water tide are evidently compensated for by the corresponding up-and-down motion of the rigid crust of the Earth, leaving only the difference of 75 centimetres apparent to observers on the seashore. *Thus, strange as it seems, the ground under our feet is periodically moving up and down with all the cities, hills, and mountains on its surface.* It is pulled up every night when the moon is high in the sky, and sinks down again as soon as the moon drops beneath the horizon. The second upward motion occurs when the moon is directly under our feet and, so to speak, pulls the entire globe down from under us. It goes without saying that this up-and-down motion proceeds so smoothly that it cannot be directly detected by even the most sensitive physical apparatus. The observed fact that the tides in rocks are about four times smaller than the tides in water indicates a comparatively high rigidity of our globe, and,

Moon and the Sun are on the same side of the Earth and are "pulling together."

* The values were observed from an isolated Pacific island which was too small to affect the motion of oceanic waters appreciably.

using the theory of elasticity, one can calculate from these data the rigidity of the Earth as a whole. By so doing, the famous English physicist Lord Kelvin was the first to arrive at the conclusion that *the rigidity of the Earth's body is as high as if it were made of good steel.* As was said above, this result does not contradict the fact that, in response to weak but persistent forces, our globe behaves just as a soft plastic body.

WHAT GOOD ARE EARTHQUAKES?

When we remember that only a very thin rocky crust, comparable to the skin of an apple, separates us from the red-hot semi-molten interior of our planet, we do not wonder that the inhabitants of its surface are so often reminded of the "physical hell" lying below the peaceful woodlands and blue seas.

Besides the terrific outbursts of volcanic activity, which eject thousands of tons of flaming lava and quantities of volcanic ash that can bury entire cities (remember the sad fate of Pompeii), the subterranean disturbances often take the form of vigorous oscillations of the crust felt all over the world. We learn from history that the cities of Lisbon and Messina were shaken into fragments by violent earthquakes, and Hollywood movies remind us vividly of the tragedy of San Francisco. During the past few years the newspapers have carried reports of major earthquake catastrophes in Chile, Turkey, and Rumania, while the name of Japan is associated with an almost continuous sequence of quakes. Remembering that all these, and a number of other major catastrophes of the same kind, occurred during a period of time that is only a wink compared with the entire life span of our planet, we become aware that the crust of the Earth is actually very far from being the "safe solid ground" it seems to be at first sight (Plate XIA).

The primary cause of all these *tectonic phenomena,* as they are called in geology, lies in the steady cooling and shrinking of our globe. As we shall see later in greater detail, the shrinking of the Earth leads to the formation of numerous wrinkles on its rocky surface, the wrinkles that we call mountains. From time to time this wrinkling process assumes a gigantic scale, and long folds of mountain ranges are raised across the previously level surfaces of the continents. The last catastrophic event of this kind occurred some twenty to forty million years ago and resulted in the formation of the Himalayan, Alpine, Rocky, and Andean ranges. From the point of view of the Earth's history twenty or forty million years is not a long period at all, and we cannot be assured that this latest revolutionary epoch of mountain-making is quite over. On the contrary, a comparison of the events of the last forty million years with the analogous revolutionary periods of the much more distant past appears to indicate that this latest mountain-building period has not yet reached its peak, and that the present epoch may be just a short breathing spell between two successive outbursts of tectonic activity.

But even now, occasional dislocations and squeezings of the weaker parts of the crust are taking place, and large quantities of molten lava are still ejected through the occasional cracks in the rocky envelope. All these processes are necessarily accompanied by more or less vigorous disturbances of the stress balance in the crust, which are propagated through the body of the Earth in the form of more or less intensive earthquake waves. In Figure 19 we give the centres of activity of the major earthquakes, from which one can see that the most pronounced quake activity takes place along the same "ring of fire" around the Pacific Ocean that is famous for the number of its active volcanoes. It is not difficult to understand the comparative weakness of the Earth's crust along this line, if we remember that it is the old scar on the

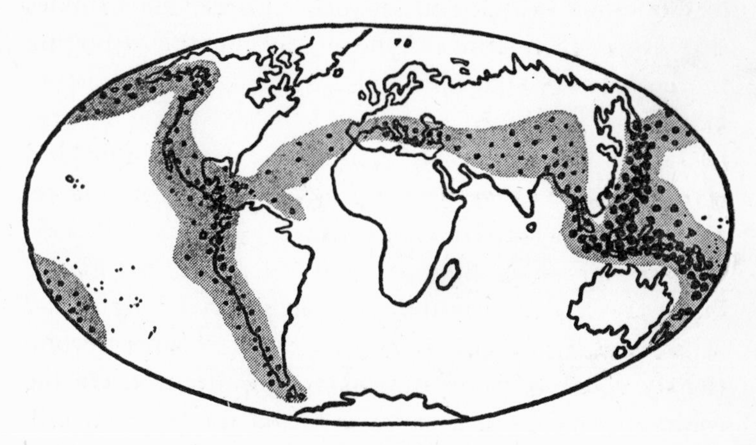

FIGURE 19
The main centres of present earthquake activity.

body of our planet representing the junction between its parts made of entirely different materials (basalt and granite).

Although earthquakes can hardly be considered pleasant events, causing as they do the loss of thousands of human lives and many millions of dollars in damage, they are very useful to the students of the Earth inasmuch as they afford us the best method of learning something about the deep interior of the Earth. Starting usually at comparatively small depths, that is, within the 50-kilometre layer of the solid crust, earthquake waves are propagated, however, right through the body of the globe and, in the case of very powerful tremors, can be noticed practically all over the world. But it must be remembered that at great distances from their origin even the most vigorous quakes can be detected only by means of a very sensitive apparatus called the seismograph.

The seismograph is based essentially on the law of inertia, according to which any body at rest tends to pre-

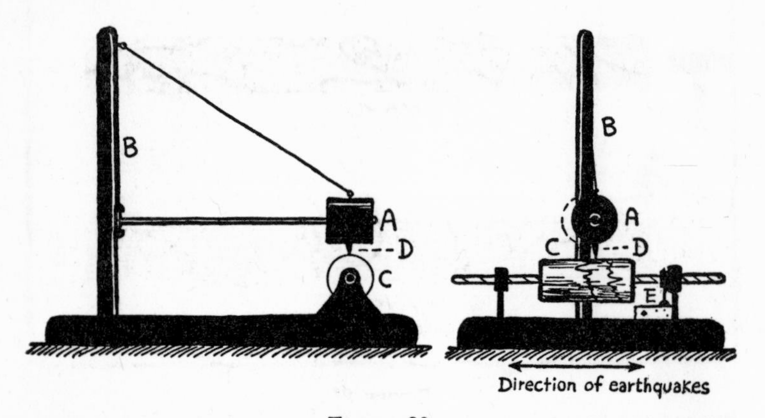

FIGURE 20
Scheme of a simple seismograph. *A:* a heavy weight suspended from a vertical pole *B; C:* a rotating cylinder driven by the clock mechanism *E; D:* a writing pen. The arrow indicates the direction of earthquakes that can be registered by this apparatus.

serve its state of rest. There are many different systems of seismographs; one of them is represented schematically in Figure 20. It consists of a heavy weight *A*, which can move with very little friction around the vertical pole *B*. If the ground on which this apparatus is installed is jerked by the earthquake wave in a direction perpendicular to the plane of the drawing, weight *A* remains immovable because of its large inertia, and the displacement of the stand relative to the weight is registered on the rotating cylinder *C*. Two such instruments installed at right angles to each other give us complete information about the horizontal displacements produced by the quake. There are, of course, other seismographs designed to register the vertical jerks of the ground and the sudden changes of inclination to a fixed direction in space.

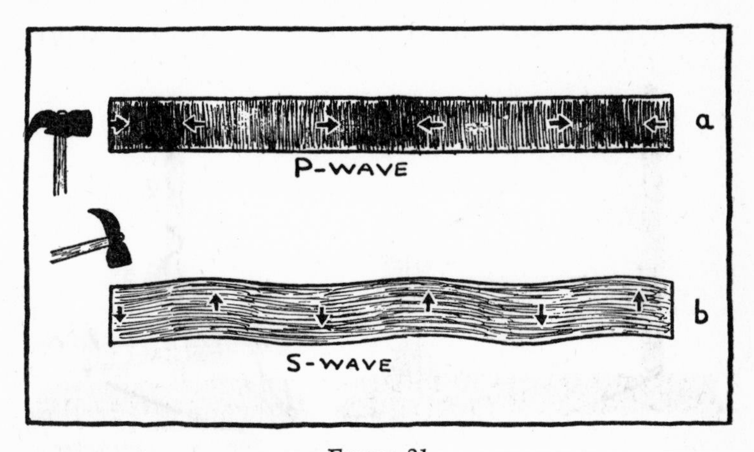

FIGURE 21
Pressure and shear waves in a solid rod. In the top bar the dark areas are regions of compression; the light areas are regions of expansion. All displacements are drawn to an exaggerated scale.

In speaking of elastic waves in solids, we must distinguish between two different types, which are usually referred to as "P-waves" (pressure waves) and "S-waves" (shear waves). The difference between these two types of waves can be easily seen from the example given in Figure 21. If we hit the end of an iron rod with a hammer (Figure 21a), the material will be compressed under the force of the impact, and this compression will be propagated along the rod in the form of a pressure wave. The different parts of the rod will move periodically to and fro in the direction of the propagation of the wave (as indicated by the small arrows in the figure), and therefore we also call such a motion a *longitudinal wave.*

A different type of wave motion is obtained if we shake the end of the rod by hitting it on the side (Figure 21b). In this case the deformation produced by the hammer will not be a compression of the material of the rod, but rather a shift of some parts relative to others. Such deformations, known as shear deformations, will also be propagated along the rod, but the motion of separate parts in this case will be perpendicular to the direction of the propagation; we speak of these as *transversal waves.* It must be clear from this description that, although the pressure waves can propagate in liquids and gases just as well as in elastic solids,* the transversal shear waves can exist only in solid bodies.

The propagation velocity of the waves depends upon the resistance of the given material to the deformations produced by the waves, and, since in any given material the resistance to compression and the resistance to shear deformations are different, the two types of waves will in general be propagated with different velocities. It happens that *in most of the known solids the velocity of the pressure waves is higher than the velocity of the shear waves,* so that, if we hit one end of the rod in an arbitrary direction, thus simultaneously producing both kinds of waves, the far end of the rod will start vibrating in the direction of its length, and only after a fraction of a second will this motion be joined by the transversal oscillations.

Exactly the same thing happens when the earthquake disturbance is propagated from the place of its origin

* Ordinarily sound waves represent the most familiar example of such longitudinal wave motion.

through the elastic body of the Earth: *the first to arrive is always the P-wave, followed after a brief interval by the second shock due to the slower S-wave.* We must remark here that the notations "P" and "S" for the two kinds of seismic waves originated actually from this fact of their earlier and later arrival, the first wave being called the "primary" and the later the "secondary." It is sheer philological coincidence that the primary waves turned out to be pressure or "push" waves as well, whereas the secondary waves can be described as sheer or "shake" waves.

The typical seismogram, that is, the record of the apparatus registering the quakes, is shown in Figure 22, where two separate groups of shocks are clearly visible. But this diagram also shows us that each of the two groups consists of three separate subgroups, which are known respectively as "P," "P-star," "P-bar," "S," "S-star," and "S-bar" waves. Since there are only two possible types of wave propagation, we must expect that *these different subgroups represent the same kind of waves propagated along paths of different length.*

In order to make the situation clearer, let us imagine two villages connected by a straight but very bad country road. Suppose also that there is an improved road, which, however, does not run through the villages, so that the person who wants to take it must cover some additional distance on connecting roads. Finally, there is a broad concrete highway, which requires, however, still larger detours to reach it. Imagine now that three cars of the same make and in the same condition, driven by equally skilful drivers, start simultaneously from the first village with the intention of reaching the second one as quickly as possible. The driver of the first car, thinking only of the shortest distance, takes the country road and, doing his best, muddles through at a speed of but little more than 30 miles per hour. The second driver chooses the improved road, and, gaining on it more than was lost on connexions, arrives at the destination before the first one. But upon his arrival he finds the driver of the third car

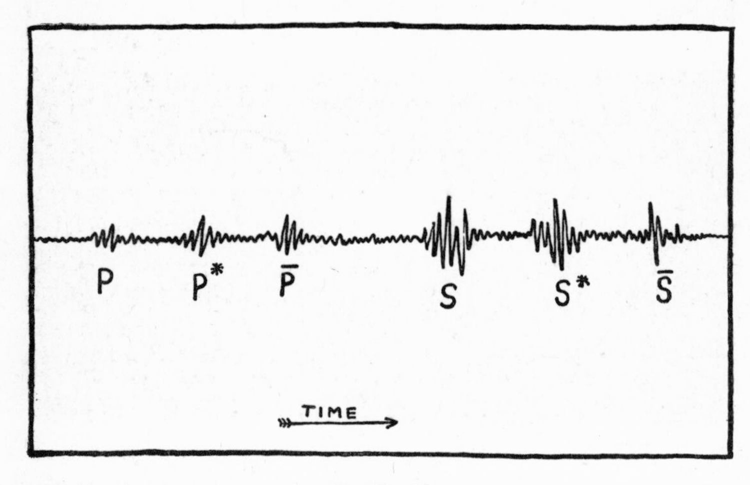

FIGURE 22
Six successive impulses arriving from a distant earthquake within the first few minutes.

sipping his Coca-Cola in the local drug store; this fellow got on the concrete highway and, in spite of the additional distance he had to cover, arrived at the village before the two others.

If we substitute earthquake waves for the cars, and the three different layers of the Earth's surface for the three roads (Figure 23), the meaning of the seismogram shown in Figure 22 becomes quite clear. The bad country road corresponds to the thin sedimentary layer, formed by the products of erosion, that covers most of the continental surfaces. The improved road will be the 50-kilometre-thick granite layer of the primitive crust, and the highway the underlying layer of the still heavier basalt. Measurements of the elastic properties of rocks really show that waves in sedimentary rocks possess the lowest velocities,

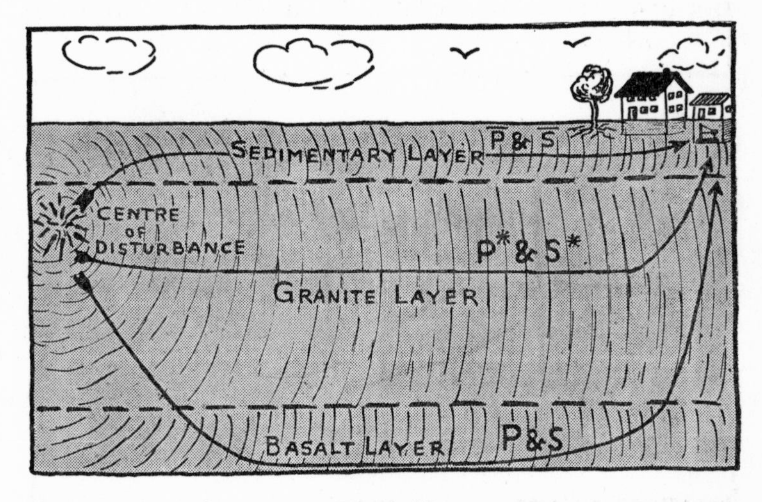

FIGURE 23
Three ways in which the earthquake waves can reach the observation station.

and waves in basalt the highest velocities. This should be expected, since the rigidity of rocks increases with their densities as a rule. To make the analogy complete, it is only necessary to add three trucks, representing the slower moving S-waves, which start from the first village simultaneously with the cars and also choose the three different roads.

Studying the arrival dates of different waves at a number of stations situated at different distances from the original disturbance, we can not only determine the velocities of separate waves, but also get an idea of the "length of the connecting roads," which in this correspond to the depths of different layers under the surface of the Earth. In Figure 24 we give, by way of example, the graph of the arrival times of a small earthquake wave,

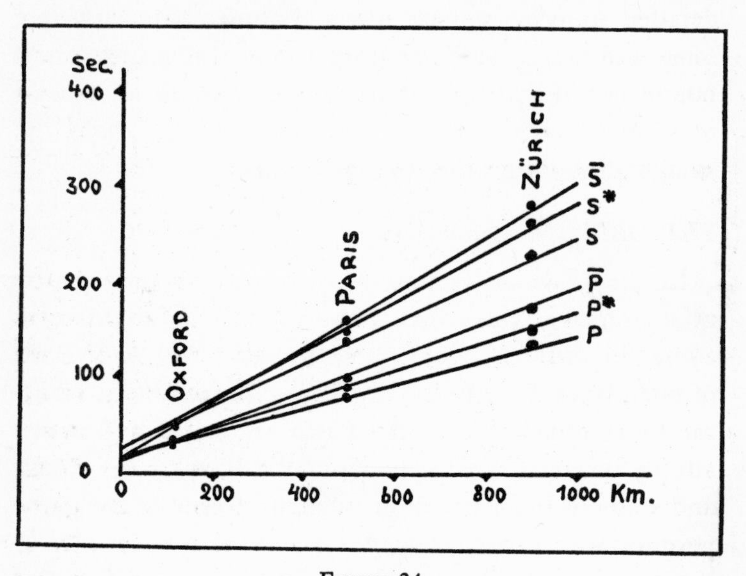

FIGURE 24
Arrival time of an earthquake originating in Hereford (England) at different distant points.

which started somewhere near Hereford, England, and was traced as far as Switzerland. We notice from this graph that the velocities of the P-wave in the three layers mentioned above are 5.6, 6.7, and 7.8 kilometres per second, respectively, whereas we get values of 3.4, 3.6, and 4.3 for the slower S-wave. We also notice that the straight lines representing different subgroups intersect at a distance of about 100 kilometres from the origin in such a way that at shorter distances the P-bar and S-bar waves (i.e., those going through the sedimentary layer) arrive first. The reason for that can also be understood from our analogy. In fact, if the two villages are very close to each other, it would be very stupid to make a long detour merely to get on a few miles of good road. More detailed study of seismic waves indicates that there are some additional discontinuities below the granite-basalt boundary, which, in the above example, would correspond to several "superhighways" still farther away from the straight line connecting the two villages.

THE DEEP INTERIOR

In the previous section we discussed the propagation of earthquake waves over comparatively short distances along the different rocky shells forming the outer crust of our planet. In cases of very strong disturbances, which can be recorded all over the Earth, the waves will naturally be propagated directly across the body of the Earth, and study of their arrival at different points of the globe permits us to penetrate with our mental eye virtually to the very centre of our planet. The most striking fact revealed by observations of such long-distance quakes is the existence of the so-called "shadow zone," that is, a broad belt on the surface of the globe in which the disturbance passes practically unnoticed. If, for example, the centre of the quake is somewhere in Peru (Figure 25), strong disturbances will be noticed all over the Western Hemisphere and also in the parts of the Eastern Hemisphere situated around the opposite pole of the quake (that is, in India, Indo-China, and the East Indies). However, the seismographs of the stations in a belt passing through northern Siberia, most of Europe, West Africa, the southern part of the Indian Ocean, south-eastern Australia, and the western part of the Pacific will behave as if nothing had happened.

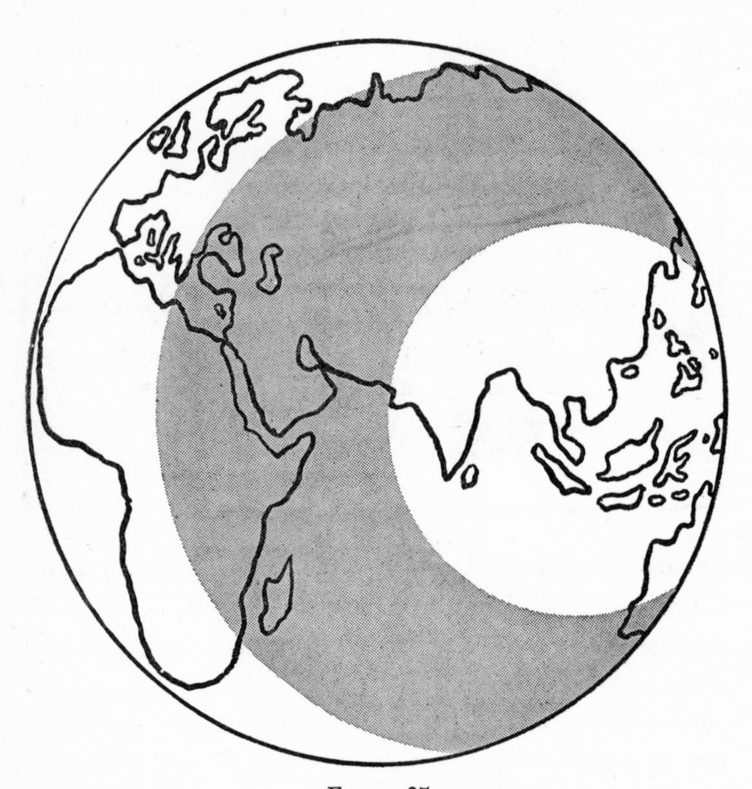

FIGURE 25
Earthquake shadow zone for a disturbance radiating from Peru (the sharpness of the zone limits is exaggerated).

This astonishing effect is due to the peculiar refraction effect experienced by the earthquake waves passing through the deep interior of the Earth; it can be easily demonstrated by means of a spherical fish bowl and a light. If we fill the fish bowl to the top and, placing it against the wall, illuminate it with the beam of light (Figure 26), we observe a ring shadow, with a brightly illuminated spot in the centre. It is easy to see that the bowl acts as an imperfect optical lens and collects all the rays falling on its surface into the central spot, leaving the surrounding region in darkness. The phenomenon of

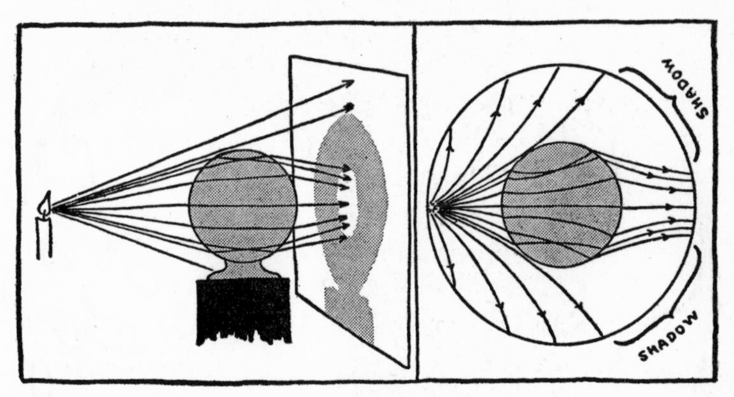

FIGURE 26
The origin of the earthquake shadow zone shown as due to the iron core of the Earth.

shadow in the case of earthquakes can be explained exactly along the same lines if we assume that the central part of the globe is formed by the spherical core consisting of material with a higher refractive power for the elastic waves than the surrounding mantle possesses. The waves of the quake disturbances passing through such a core will be refracted in the very same way as the rays of light passing through the fish bowl, and will be "focused" at the point of the Earth's surface directly opposite the place of original disturbance.

From the observed extent of the "shadow" we can calculate the size of this central refracting core; we find that it extends to about one-half (more exactly 0.6) of the Earth's radius. The high refractive power of this core indicates that *it must be made of considerably denser material than the surrounding mantle,* which is in excellent agreement with the well-known fact that the mean density of the Earth (estimated from its total mass and total volume) is much higher than the density of the rocks on its surface. Studying the propagation of earthquake waves through the core of the Earth, we can reach some very important conclusions about its physical and chemical nature. First of all, the density of the core, as estimated from the propagation velocity of the waves, is found to be between 10 and 12 times the density of water, which strongly supports the hypothesis that *the central part of our planet, about one-eighth in volume, consists of almost pure iron.* The reader may remember in this connexion that the meteorites that fall on the surface of the Earth from interplanetary space and most probably represent pieces of some broken planet can be divided into two different classes: the iron meteorites, containing up to 90 per cent of pure iron; and the stone meteorites, analogous in their chemical composition to the igneous rocks of the Earth's surface.* The conclusion seems inescapable that the difference between these two types of meteorites is due to their having originated at different depths of the unfortunate planet.

The second important point about this iron core of our planet is disclosed by observation of the type of elastic waves that can be propagated through it. It seems that,

* Meteorites analogous in their constitution to the sedimentary rocks formed by the erosion processes on the Earth's surface have never been found. This must, however, be expected, since sedimentary layers represent but a negligible part of the total mass of a planet.

unlike other parts of the Earth, the core is absolutely unable to transmit the transversal shear waves, and that only the waves of compression can pass through it. This indicates that *the iron of the core is in the liquid state;*

FIGURE 27
The Earth, with a segment of the solid outer crust and the plastic mantle cut away, showing the central iron core.

not a viscous plastic mass like the rocks forming the mantle, but in a truly fluid state similar to the molten iron pouring from the openings of the blast furnaces in our steel mills. Remembering the explanation given above for the plastic properties of materials under very high pressures, we must conclude that the atoms of iron are probably more slippery than the molecules of different chemical compounds that comprise the rocks, so that even when strongly compressed they retain most of their mobility.

To recapitulate, *the body of our planet consists of a number of concentric shells of different materials arranged in the order of increasing density*. There is a thin, rigid crust of solidified granites and basalts, a thick layer of semi-molten plastic basalt and heavier rocks underneath, and finally a soft molten iron core in the centre (Figure 27). A golf player would probably compare the structure of our globe with that of a golf ball, which also has a thin, rigid envelope, a thick layer of rubber bands, and finally a central core made of honey.* This separation of materials in the body of the Earth took place in its early youth, when it was still quite liquid or even gaseous, and the heavier parts, iron in particular, easily sank to the centre. It will remain so for all time to come, unless our planet is broken to bits by some unexpected direct or indirect collision with some other celestial body.

THE MYSTERY OF THE COMPASS NEEDLE

Of all the properties connected with the internal structure of our globe the existence of its magnetic field represents one of the best-known but also one of the most mysterious phenomena. The knowledge that the iron needle, treated in a certain way, can indicate the direction of the Pole has existed in China for countless centuries and was

* The sedimentary layers and the soil can be compared with the dirt covering the surface of a golf ball.

brought to Europe by Marco Polo among many other Oriental rarities. The study of the distribution of the magnetic field over the surface of the Earth and of its periodic variations with time occupies many marine and purely scientific institutions, and its mathematical description, begun by the famous German mathematician Karl Friedrich Gauss, fills many bulky volumes.

However, up to the present time, we still do not know what causes this magnetic field, and according to our best knowledge of the properties of the Earth's interior it should not be there at all! In fact, investigation of the magnetic properties of different substances, such as iron and nickel, proves quite definitely that any trace of magnetization must completely disappear as soon as these substances are heated above the so-called Curie point. Since the temperature inside the Earth reaches values much above the Curie point, one can hardly expect that the observed phenomena can be explained as the result of permanent magnetization. In particular, the most natural hypothesis, according to which the source of terrestrial magnetism is situated in the central iron core, can hardly stand up because seismological evidence seems to show that this iron is completely molten. It is true, of course, that under the very high pressures which turn melted rocks into a plastic mass the magnetic properties of iron and other materials can be considerably modified, and they can remain magnetic even at much higher temperatures. An elaborate compression machine constructed recently in the Carnegie Institution of Washington, which permits the study of the properties of matter at pressures up to 220,000 atmospheres (equivalent to the pressure at a depth of 480 kilometres under the surface of the Earth!), gives us certain indications in this direction. However, even if materials at great depths do possess magnetic properties, the question of the original causes of observed magnetization still remains open.

Another group of hypotheses proposed for the explanation of terrestrial magnetism considers the Earth not as a "permanent magnet" created once upon a time by unknown forces, but rather as an "electromagnet" that is being fed by some electric current now flowing through the Earth's body. Yet difficulties arise here too as soon as we ask about the origin of these currents, and all attempts made in this direction, including several very recent ones,* have not led to any satisfactory result.

Thus we must confess that *we still do not know why the magnetic needle* points north, and seamen should be glad that the compass still does its job in spite of all theoretical considerations showing that it really should not!

There can, however, be no doubt that the ultimate solution of the "mystery of the magnetic needle" will not require any revolutionary changes in our concepts of the laws of physics or the structure of the Earth, and that the difficulty of the problem lies entirely in the great complexity of the phenomena encountered at the unusual physical conditions existing far below our feet.

* The most recent attempt to explain terrestrial magnetism by convective currents in the Earth's body was made by Elsasser. According to his views, convective currents in the deep interior of the Earth produce an uneven heating of the crust and thus cause thermoelectric currents to flow along the equator. It seems, however, that the convective currents in the Earth are too slow to produce the expected effect.

CHAPTER VI

The Rise and Fall of Mountains

THE COOLING OF THE EARTH

ACCORDING to the picture of the Earth's birth described in the previous chapters, the young Earth was first in a gaseous state and later entirely molten, so that its different component materials could easily move from place to place by means of convective currents. It was during this period of the Earth's history that the heavier elements, iron in particular, sank toward the centre of the globe, while the lighter materials, such as basalt and granite, rose to the surface, thus forming the concentric shells characterizing the present structure of our planet. During this epoch of convective currents, the Earth was also cooling off very fast; streams of hot matter from the interior were rising toward the surface and, after being cooled down by radiation of heat into surrounding space, sinking back again toward the centre. This rapid cooling of our infant planet, however, progressively increased its viscosity, and the convective currents steadily slowed down. When they finally became so slow that the heat brought by them to the surface could no longer compensate for the losses through radiation, a solid crust began to form on the surface of the Earth. As we have said, the solid crust was most probably formed within a few thousand years after the separation of the Earth from the Sun. The birth of the Moon broke the crust up into several pieces, and some of these pieces were taken away to form the body of our satellite. But this little accident caused only a very short delay in the growth of the crust, and very soon after the separation of the Moon the freshly exposed surface of molten basalt solidified again, anchoring the granite pieces of the old crust.

The increasing viscosity of the Earth's materials and the formation of the solid crust must have retarded the cooling process considerably; the heat now had to be transported to the surface by the much slower process of thermal conduction. Under these conditions, the surface of our planet rapidly assumed a temperature determined solely by the amount of solar radiation falling on it during the daytime, while the ocean basins filled up with water.

Slow though it was, the cooling process was penetrating deeper and deeper beneath the surface of the Earth, and, as we have seen, the solid crust grew to the impressive thickness of 40 to 50 kilometres.

A very important factor in the Earth's cooling is the amount of heat flowing out through its rocky crust. This amount can be easily estimated from the existing temperature differences in the crust, 30° C. (54° F.) per kilometre, and the measured thermal conductivity of its constituent rocks. It has been found that the amount of heat rising from below through each square centimetre of the Earth's surface is extremely small—it is thirty million times smaller than the amount of solar heat falling on the same surface from above. If we were to place a glass of ice-cold water on the surface of the Earth and insulate it so that it would collect only the heat coming from below, it would take about thirty years for the water to be heated to the boiling point. If all the heat flowing from the crust of the Earth came from the cooling of its interior (and we shall see in the next section that most of this heat is due to radioactive processes), *it would take about one hundred million years to cool the Earth by one degree C.*

Thus the mean cooling of the Earth's body cannot have amounted to more than 20° C. since the formation of the solid crust some five billion years ago! The reader will understand, of course, that since the Earth is being cooled only at its surface, the drop in temperature is distributed unevenly through its body; whereas the temperature in the deep interior has remained almost unchanged during these five billion years, the temperature of the thin surface layer must have dropped from the melting point of rocks to its present low value.

RADIOACTIVITY OF THE EARTH'S CRUST

We have just said that a considerable portion of the heat flowing out through the crust of the Earth is due, not to the actual cooling of its interior, but to the presence of small quantities of radioactive substances that liberate heat in the process of their slow, spontaneous decay. The rocks comprising the crust of the Earth always contain certain amounts of uranium and thorium, and we saw in Chapter I how study of the decay products of these elements enables us to estimate the age of these rocks. With the exception of a few minerals, such as the Bohemian pitchblende used by Madame Curie in isolating radium, the concentration of radioactive materials in rocks is extremely low. One ton of ordinary granite contains, for example, only 9 grammes of uranium and 20 grammes of thorium, while there is even less in basaltic rocks (3.5 and 7.7 grammes per ton of basalt). In addition to their exceedingly low concentration, these elements all have extremely slow rates of subatomic energy liberation. The energy liberated by one ton of pure uranium in thirty years would be hardly enough to heat a cup of coffee.*

However, in spite of their low concentration and minute rate of energy liberation, radioactive materials play an essential role in the total heat balance of the Earth; it has been calculated that these materials in the outer crust alone can account for most of the total heat flow near the surface. If we assumed that the percentage of uranium and thorium in the deeper interior of the Earth is the same as in the surface rocks, the total energy liberation due to radioactive processes would greatly exceed the observed amount of heat flowing through the crust. This result forces us to presuppose that *the radioactive elements are, for some reason or other, confined solely to the comparatively thin outer layer, and that the interior of the Earth is entirely devoid of any trace of radioactivity.* This conclusion is in agreement with the fact that the concentration of uranium and thorium in the underlying basalt layer begins to be somewhat lower than the corresponding concentration in the outer layer of granite (compare the numerical values on page 111). Moreover, examination of meteorites reveals that the radioactivity of iron meteorites, which must have originated from the interior of the solar system's shattered planet, is much lower than that of ordinary stone meteorites.

* The total subatomic energy stored inside uranium atoms is enormous, and in this sense one ton of uranium is equivalent to one million tons of good coal. But the trouble is that this energy leaks out so slowly; it takes several billion years to release one-half of the amount stored.

The most plausible explanation of the high concentration of radioactive elements in the outer layers of the Earth assumes that it dates back to the time when the Earth was entirely molten, and that at that time the materials containing radioactive elements rose to the surface simply because they had been warmed up by the heat developed in the process of radioactive decay.

In any case, science today must be very grateful to nature for the concentration of radioactive elements in the outer layers of the Earth. If these elements were distributed uniformly throughout the body of our planet, their concentration in the surface rocks would be thousands of times lower than it is now, and the phenomenon of radioactivity might well have remained undiscovered even up to the present time.

HOW HOT IS THE CENTRE OF THE EARTH?

The problem of temperature distribution in the body of the Earth beyond the depth of a few kilometres, where it can be directly measured, presents very serious difficulties because we have no reliable data concerning the distribution of radioactive elements at greater depths and because we do not know the thermal conductivity of rocks under very high pressures and temperatures. As we have noted, most of the heat flow through the outer layers of the crust is due to the radioactivity of the outer crust's rocks, so that the heat flow must be considerably smaller in the deeper interior, where the concentration of radioactive materials drops almost to zero. Correspondingly, the rate of temperature change with depth should be reduced materially.

Making plausible assumptions about the distribution of radioactive materials in the outer crust,* and also assuming that the thermal conductivity of the rocks in the inner regions does not differ essentially from that observed at the surface, one can calculate the temperature distribution at depths that are far beyond the reach of any direct measurement. The rise in temperature, which is very rapid in the first few dozen kilometres, becomes much slower at greater depths, so that in the interior of the Earth the temperature increases at the rate of only 3° C. (5.4° F.) per kilometre (i.e., 10 times slower than in the outer crust). *Continuing this curve all the way to the centre we find the central temperature of the Earth to be several thousand degrees,* i.e., about the same as the surface temperature of the Sun. It must be remembered that all calculations of this sort are necessarily very inexact, and that different authors give rather different values for the central temperature of our planet.

Whereas the temperature on the surface of the Earth has dropped more than 1000° C. (1800° F.) since the Earth first began to cool down, the temperature drop at the depth of 30 kilometres is found to have totalled only 800° C. (1440° F.), while at the depth of 400 kilometres matter has remained at almost the same temperature it had when the solid crust was just beginning to form. All this indicates that *during the last five billion years the temperature of most of the Earth has remained practically unchanged, and that the cooling effect has been confined to the outer parts of its body.*

* It is usually assumed that the concentration of radioactive elements decreases by half for each 20 kilometres of depth.

PLATE I. The spiral nebula in Ursa Major, consisting of many billions of separate stars. Our own stellar system, the Milky Way, would look very much like this if seen from the outside, and our Sun would be merely one of the multitudinous stars. (*Courtesy of the Mt. Wilson Observatory*)

PLATE IIA (see p. 9). Halley's comet, photographed May 4, 1910.

PLATE IIB (see p. 31). Zodiacal light, with star trails, photographed March 17, 1928.

PLATE III (see p. 52). Photograph of the full Moon, showing the darker areas ("maria") and the lunar craters, with "light rays" diverging from some of the latter. *(Courtesy of the Yerkes Observatory)*

PLATE IV (see p. 52). Photograph of a part of the Moon's surface, showing the detailed structure of its craters. *(Courtesy of the Yerkes Observatory)*

PLATE VA (see p. 65). A phase of Venus. The brilliancy of this planet is due to the high reflecting power of the thick clouds covering its daylight atmosphere. *(Courtesy of the Yerkes Observatory)*

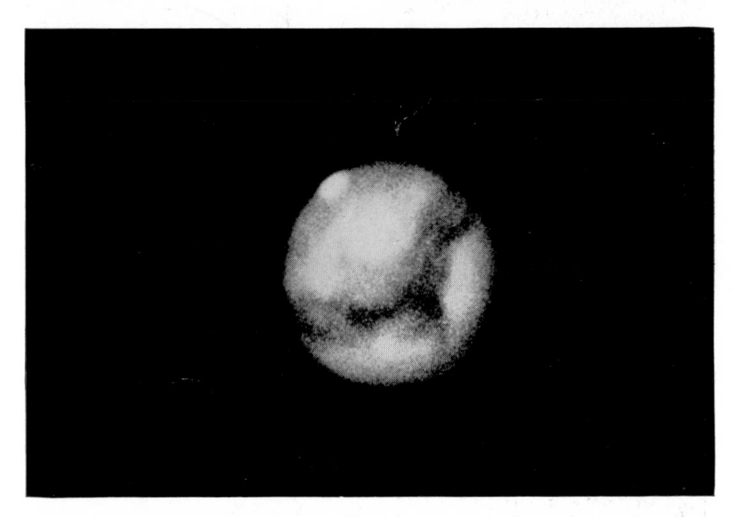

PLATE VB (see p. 72). Photograph of Mars during its closest approach to the Earth, September 28, 1909. The white spot at the top is the polar ice cap. The lighter parts of the surface represent deserts, while the darker ones are probably lowlands covered with vegetation.

(Courtesy of the Yerkes Observatory)

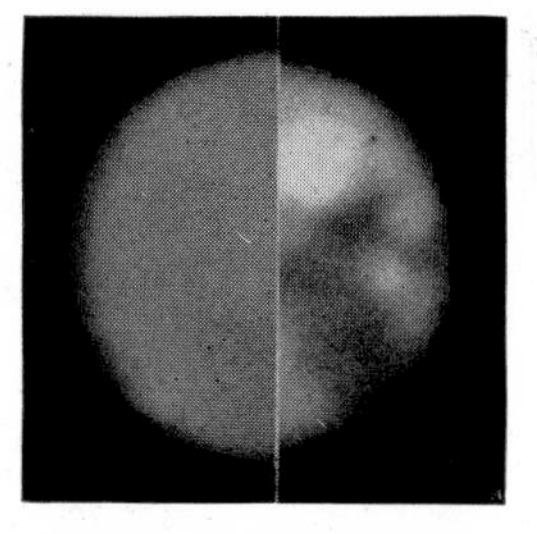
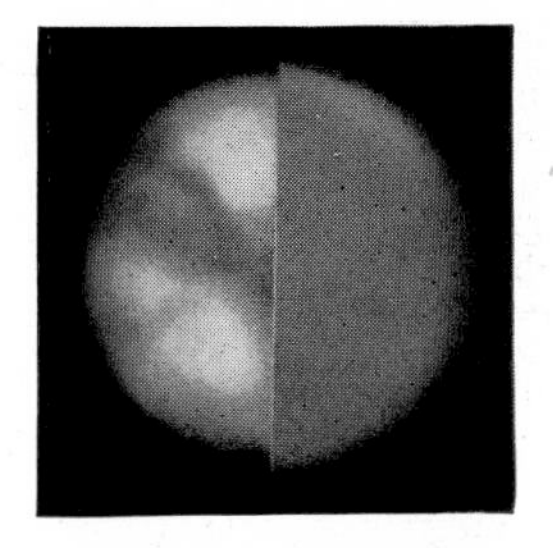

PLATE VIA (see p. 65). Two views of Mars, in which one-half of the planet was photographed by ultraviolet light and the other by infrared light. Since infrared rays are easily reflected from the atmosphere, the larger size of the infrared image shows the extent of the Martian atmosphere.
(Courtesy of the Lick Observatory)

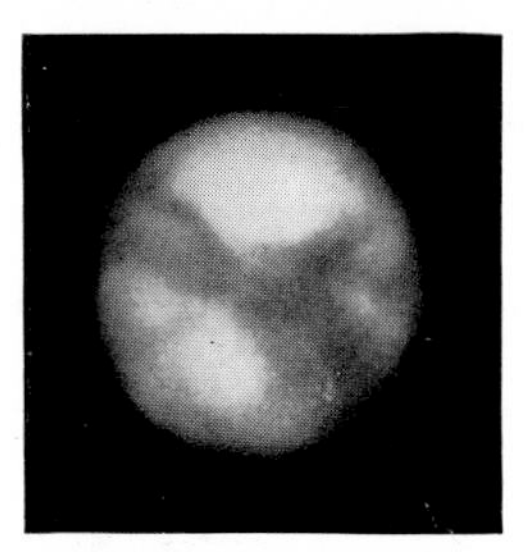
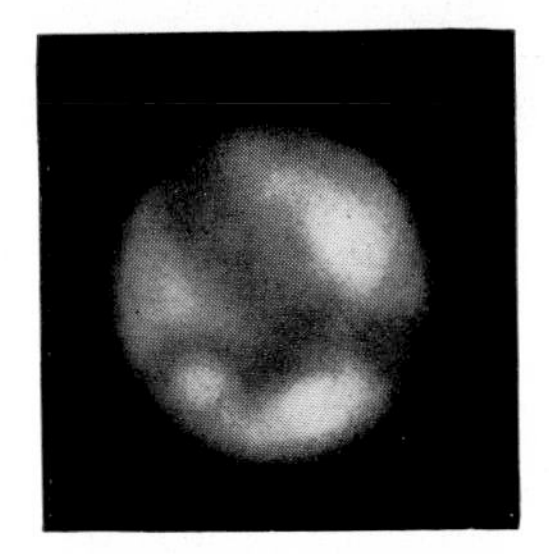

PLATE VIB (see p. 65). A cloud in Mars's atmosphere, seen as a little white spot in the photograph at the left. In the second photograph, taken the next day, the cloud has completely disappeared.
(Courtesy of the Lick Observatory)

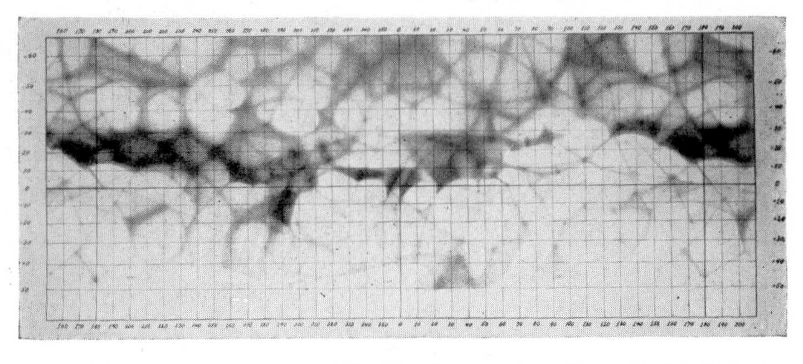

PLATE VIC (see p. 75). A map of the Martian canals as drawn by R. J. Trumpler from visual observation in 1924. More recent observations prove the canals to be optical illusions. *(Courtesy of the Lick Observatory)*

PLATE VII (see p. 67). Photograph of Jupiter, showing horizontal strata of atmospheric origin. The surface of the planet itself has never been seen.
(Courtesy of the Mt. Wilson Observatory)

PLATE VIII (see p. 67). Photograph of Saturn, showing atmospheric strata like those on Jupiter. The ring is formed by a large number of small meteorites revolving around the planet and probably representing the fragments of one of its former satellites. *(Courtesy of the Mt. Wilson Observatory)*

PLATE IX (see p. 79). "Old Faithful," a geyser in Yellowstone National Park (photographed at night). Periodic eruptions of hot water and steam are due to the fact that the water from the surface of the Earth leaks down through cracks in the crust and, reaching a depth of more than 2 kilometres, is heated to the boiling point by contact with the hot rocks of the interior.

(Courtesy of the U.S. Geologic Survey)

PLATE X (see p. 79). The eruption of the volcano Vesuvius, April 1872. Molten basaltic material from a depth of about 50 kilometres is forced up to the surface through occasional cracks in the solid crust of the Earth. The temperature of the lava coming from the crater is about 1200° C. (2200° F.).

(Courtesy of the U.S. Geologic Survey)

PLATE XIA (see p. 92). Deep cracks in the surface of the Earth produced by a violent earthquake. *(Courtesy of the U.S. Geologic Survey)*

PLATE XIB (see p. 115). The bent lines of sedimentary layers of rock clearly indicate that the mountains were formed as the result of horizontal compression of the Earth's crust. *(Courtesy of the U.S. Geologic Survey)*

PLATE XII (see p. 125). Fantastic shapes produced by the action of rain water in the Bad Lands of South Dakota. Note the vertical columns, which remained standing because their material was compressed somewhat more bv the weight of the rocks that are seen on top of each column.

(Courtesy of the U.S. Geologic Survey)

PLATE XIIIA (see p. 125). The Devil's Tower, in South Dakota, was formed by the lava solidified in the crater of an old extinct volcano. The volcanic cone itself was washed away completely by rain water.

(Courtesy of the U.S. Geologic Survey)

PLATE XIIIB (see p. 125). The canyon in Yellowstone National Park formed in the volcanic plateau by the erosive action of the river.

(Courtesy of the U.S. Geologic Survey)

PLATE XIVA (see p. 165). The "ice river" of a glacier descending a mountain slope. *(Courtesy of the U.S. Geologic Survey)*

PLATE XIVB (see p. 167). A large stone, once carried by a glacier, now resting on the rocky ground polished by ice during the last glacial period. (Not far from New York City!) *(Courtesy of the U.S. Geologic Survey)*

PLATE XV (see pp. 142, 212). Reading the "Book of Sediments." Some pages of the Jurassic chapter, found in Solenhofen, Bavaria, which revealed the skeleton of the first bird, known as the archæopteryx. The sketch in the lower left corner gives the reconstruction of this creature. *(Courtesy of the U.S. National Museum)*

PLATE XVI (see p. 204). A piece of sandstone dating back to the Cambrian period (*ca.* 400,000,000 B.C.). The tracks seen on its surface are not due to a prehistoric automobile, but were produced by large worms crawling across the wet sand. Note the markings left by the waves.

(Courtesy of the U.S. National Museum)

PLATE XVII (see p. 205). Fossils of trilobites in the deposits of the Devonian period (*ca.* 250,000,000 B.C.)—natural size.

(Courtesy of the U.S. National Museum)

PLATE XVIIIA (see p. 210). The giant dinosaur *Tyrannosaurus rex* (about 12 feet high), which populated North America during the Cretaceous period (*ca.* 70,000,000 B.C.). *(Courtesy of the American Museum of Natural History)*

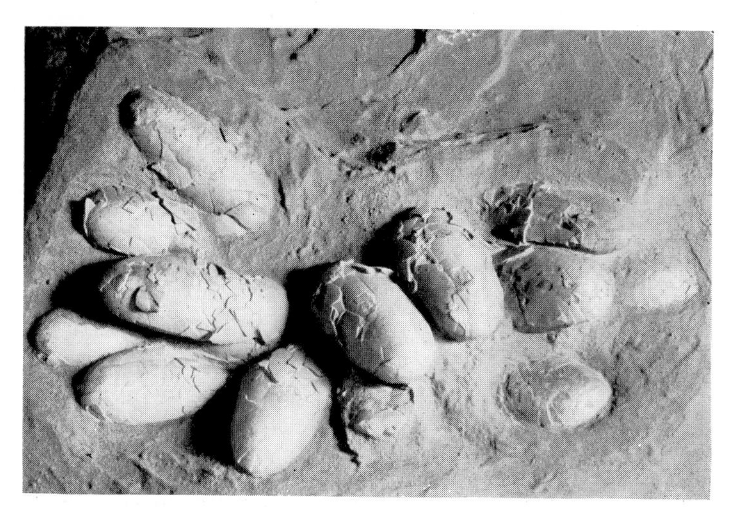

PLATE XVIIIB (see p. 211). Eggs of the dinosaur protoceratops, preserved in the sands of the Gobi Desert in Mongolia.
(Courtesy of the American Museum of Natural History)

PLATE XIX (see p. 205). Ocean shore, Early Palæozoic era, strewn with wave-borne seaweed and shells. Long, tube-like forms are Silurian straight-shelled cephalopods; snail-shaped forms are round-shelled cephalopods. Trilobites (lower right) would be seen scurrying across the sand. Though marine life had progressed considerably, the land was virtually uninhabited except for some species of millepedes and scorpions.

(Courtesy of the Field Museum of Natural History)

PLATE XX (see p. 209). Woods of the Middle Palæozoic era were mostly in marshlands and consisted chiefly of giant horsetails, ferns, and club mosses. Carbonized remains of these forest giants constitute present coal deposits.

(Courtesy of the Field Museum of Natural History)

PLATE XXI (see p. 208). Certain Early Permian reptiles resembled today's crocodiles. Others had high, bony dorsal fins, probably for defence. Their feet were at their sides; movement on land was slow and sprawling.

(Courtesy of the Field Museum of Natural History)

PLATE XXII (see p. 211). The diplodocus, its near relative the brontosaurus (weight about 50 tons; 70 feet from nose to tail), or the giant stegosaurus (with heavy armour-plate along the spine) might easily be met in the woods of the Jurassic period. *(Courtesy of the U.S. National Museum)*

PLATE XXIII (see pp. 210, 211). *Tyrannosaurus rex,* a giant kangaroo-like reptile, terror of the Cretaceous period. The same period saw an abundance of horned reptiles; triceratops is the largest known representative of this class. *(Courtesy of the Field Museum of Natural History)*

PLATE XXIV (see p. 212). Mesozoic waters abounded with various marine reptiles. Most typical were the ichthyosaurus, generally fish-like in form, and the plesiosaurus, with long, swan-like neck useful for fishing.
(Courtesy of the Field Museum of Natural History)

PLATE XXV (see p. 212). Pterodactyls (upper left), "air force" of the great middle kingdom of reptiles, had naked bodies, leathery wings, and sharp teeth. During the Cretaceous period these flying monsters attained maximum development; some fossil specimens show 25-foot wing-spread. Prehistoric turtle at lower right

(Courtesy of the Field Museum of Natural History)

PLATE XXVI (see p. 218). The entelodonts (giant boars), probably the most powerful animals of the Miocene period, were as big as oxen and had skulls 4 feet long. About 2,000,000 years ago the rhinoceros (left background) was a slender beast no bigger than an average dog. The horses of that time (centre background) were no larger than today's Shetland ponies, while the prehistoric camels (left background) resembled today's gazelles.

(Courtesy of the Field Museum of Natural History)

PLATE XXVII (see p. 219). One of the most impressive sights of the glacial periods must have been a family of long-tusked mammoths, covered with thick brown wool, making their way through the deep snow then blanketing large areas of Asia, Europe, and North America.

(Courtesy of the Field Museum of Natural History)

THE WRINKLES ON THE EARTH'S FACE

Although the cooling of the Earth has scarcely commenced as far as the entire body of the planet is concerned, it has played, and is playing an important role in the development of the Earth's surface features. In fact, since the outer crust of the Earth has been rigid from the very first moment of its formation, the steady cooling and subsequent contraction of the underlying plastic layers is steadily making the crust too large to fit the shrinking interior, and it must wrinkle in the very same way as the skin of an apple does in the process of baking. It is hardly necessary to tell the reader that the various wrinkles and folds formed on the surface of our planet as the result of cooling are, of course, the great mountain chains contributing so much to the beauty of the landscape (Plate XIB).

We have seen that the temperature on the surface must have dropped by about 1200° C. (2160° F.) since the formation of the outer crust, whereas it remained practically unchanged at the depth of 400 kilometres. Hence we can say that the "mean cooling" of the outer 400-kilometres-thick layer of our planet since the formation of the crust totals about 600° C. (1080° F.). From the known thermal expansion of rocks we determine that such a temperature decrease must have caused the cooled layer to shrink approximately 6 per cent in volume. Since most of this material is still in the plastic state, the cooling must have been accompanied by the continuous redistribution of plastic masses, and the total thickness of the layer must have been steadily decreasing in proportion to its volume.

Assuming the value of 400 kilometres as the total thickness of the cooled layer, we find that it must have been reduced by about 24 kilometres (6 per cent of 400 km.), while *the circumference of our globe at present is about 150 kilometres shorter than it was when the solid crust was first formed.* The total surface area of the Earth must have been reduced by 4,000,000 square kilometres, and since the mean thickness of the solid crust throughout the Earth's history can be assumed to have been about 25 kilometres,* we conclude that *not less than 100 million cubic kilometres of solid rocks must have been pushed out above the surface of the Earth in the form of various mountain ranges and high plateaux.* Even after allowing for the fact that much of this material has sunk into the plastic mass underneath, we can be sure that this quantity of pushed-up rock is quite enough to account not only for all the existing mountains of the globe, but also for all the mountains of past geological epochs that are now completely obliterated from the surface of the Earth. In fact, this volume of excrescent rock is about equal to the total volume of the continents (including all the mountains, plateaux, and lowlands) protruding above sea level.†

The above considerations, however, do not necessarily imply that the thermal contraction of the Earth's body is the only agent responsible for mountain formation. It

* The thickness of 25 kilometres is obtained here as the average between the present thickness of about 50 kilometres and the zero thickness at the beginning of the formation of the crust.

† From the known areas and mean elevations of the continents (Asia: 44,000,000 km. × 0.96 km.; Europe: 10,000,000 km. × 0.34 km.; Africa: 30,000,000 km. × 0.75 km.; North America: 24,000,000 km. × 0.72 km.; South America: 18,000,000 km. × 0.59 km.; Australia: 9,000,000 km. × 0.34 km.; and Antarctica: 14,000,000 km. × 2.2 km.) we find that the total continental volume above sea level is just about 100,000,000 cubic kilometres.

is not impossible that in certain cases the wrinkling of the surface may have been due to local movements of the crust caused, for example, by the increasing weight of accumulated sedimentary material. Such secondary mountain-formation processes must necessarily be merely local in character, and there is hardly any doubt that the great mountain ranges crossing the surface of the Earth are largely due to the most general cooling process.

SOME DETAILS OF MOUNTAIN FOLDING

In order to follow the processes of mountain folding in some detail, and, in particular, to understand the behaviour of land and sea during the revolutionary epochs when the crust shakes and crumples all over the world, we must first bear in mind that the surface of our globe consists of two entirely different types of rocks: granite rocks forming the continents, and basalt rocks forming the ocean beds.

Laboratory investigations show that basalt is considerably stronger than granite, from which it follows that most of the crumpling in the wrinkling process must be limited to the continental areas. This is in agreement with the observational evidence, which indicates that the mountain-folding activity is largely confined to the surfaces of the continents. Moreover, the weakest places of the Earth's solid crust are evidently situated along the junction lines of its granite and basaltic regions, which accounts for the very pronounced volcanic and mountain-raising activity along the continental shore lines. In particular, the ring of mountains and active volcanoes surrounding the basin of the Pacific Ocean (the "ring of fire") is obviously attributable to the comparative weakness of the scar left by the birth of the Moon.

In Figure 28 we give a schematic view of what must happen to a granite continental block compressed on all sides between the layers of solid basalt forming the bottom of the surrounding oceans. The first effect of the compression will evidently be a slow bending of the granite layer, resulting in a general uplift of its surface above the level of the surrounding ocean (Figure 28b). During this "bending-up" process the central regions of the continent are obviously not in a state of isostatic equilibrium, and the weight of the elevated portion is largely supported by the rigidity of the continent's constituent rocks.

As the cooling and compression continue, the bending of the continent progressively increases, and the internal stresses in the crust grow larger and larger, until they finally reach the breaking point of granite. The rocks forming the crust are no longer able to resist the increasing pressure, the crust breaks and crumples, and the "top of the dome" begins to fall in (Figure 28c). This collapse of the continental dome occurs very slowly, of course, because it must be accompanied by the extrusion of the plastic material from below, and, as we have seen above, all movements in the viscous plastic layer of our globe are bound to be extremely slow. It may take millions of years before the central parts of the continent, uplifted by the previous contraction, return to their original level; when this state is finally reached, the surface will be covered by numerous high ranges of crumpled and folded rocks formed from the excess material.

As we have seen, the total decrease of the Earth's circumference due to cooling must have amounted to 150 kilometres, that is, about 0.5 per cent of the total length of the equator. If we take a piece of granite and subject

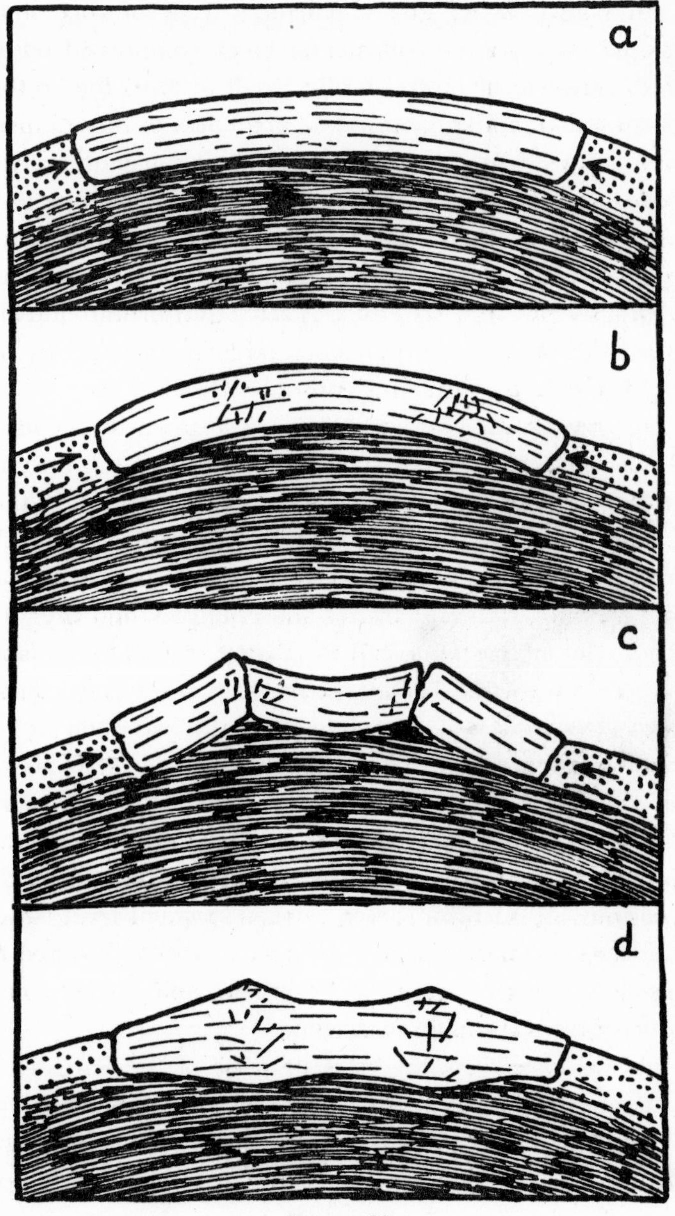

FIGURE 28
Formation of mountain folds as the result of the compression of the continental massifs.

it to high compression in a hydraulic press, we find that the rock will crack and break into separate fragments at a compressive contraction only one-fifth as great. It is therefore evident that *the granite blocks comprising the continents must have been crushed at least five consecutive times during the two billion years of the steady contraction of the Earth's crust, so that there must have been at least five great epochs of mountain-folding activity.*

If we remember that the compression of the Earth's crust must have been largely confined to the regions of continental massifs owing to the greater strength of basalt, and that there certainly must have been some places in the granite layer where the strength of the rocks was lower than the average,* we must at least double the total number of such epochs of high tectonic activity.

As we shall see in Chapter VII, the findings of historical geology are in close agreement with these conclusions concerning the periodicity of the mountain-formation process and with the general picture of the formation and collapse of the continental domes given here.

UPSIDE-DOWN MOUNTAINS

When we look at a high mountain range rising thousands of feet above the surrounding plain, we are inclined to consider it merely a gigantic excrescence of rock piled on the surface of the Earth, much like an artificial hill constructed by engineers. Such a primitive point of view, which regards mountains as wholly a surface feature, was quite common in scientific geology a century ago; only comparatively recently was it recognized that *the bulk of*

* For example, along the old soldered cracks in the interior of the continents and along the ocean shore.

any mountain is situated under the surface of the Earth.

The discovery of these "mountain roots," going very deep under the surface, resulted from the study of the gravitational action of a mountain upon two pendulums suspended on opposite sides of it. One would expect that, in accordance with the general law of gravity, the great mass of the mountain would deflect the pendulums from the vertical to an extent proportional to the size of the mountain. Of course, in this instance the word "vertical" is defined, not as a plumb line, but in respect to a fixed direction in space as given by observation of the stars. To the great surprise of the scientists who carried out such measurements for the first time, the observed deviations of the pendulums caused by the proximity of a mountain turned out to be much smaller than was expected on the basis of the mountain's size.*

In the case of Mount Everest, for example, the observed deviation is about three times smaller than should be expected from its giant mass, while the Pyrenees even seem to repel the pendulum instead of attracting it! The absence of the expected gravitational attraction clearly indicated that a certain amount of mass was lacking, inside or under the mountain, which led to the hypothesis that mountains were hollow: something like a broken eggshell placed on a table (Figure 29a).

It must be clear to a reader who has carefully followed our argument up to this point that this "eggshell" hypothesis can hardly stand up under criticism based on our present knowledge of the properties of the Earth's crust, and that the true explanation of the apparently missing

* The expected deviation can, of course, be easily calculated from Newton's law and the apparent mass of the mountain as obtained from its volume and the density of its constituent rocks.

mass under the mountain must lie in deformations of the crust by the weight of the material piled on it. According to present views, the mountains on the surface of the Earth represent formations similar to the ice hills produced on the polar ice fields by the compression of ice. Every arctic explorer knows that when blocks of ice,

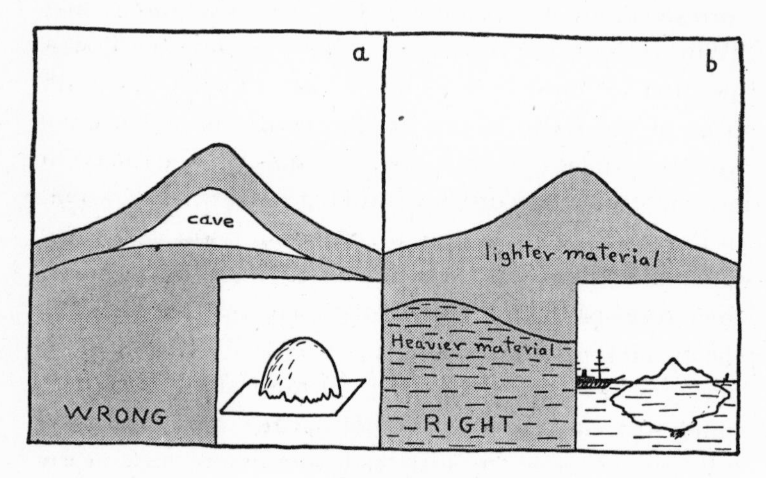

FIGURE 29
"Eggshell" and "iceberg" theories of mountain structure.

broken by compression, are piled on top of one another, most of the ice sinks below the water in order to keep the rest afloat (Figure 29b). Thus, while a polar bear will see a high hill rising above the surface of the ice field, a seal swimming under it will notice an even larger bulge protruding into the water. Similarly, *to each mountain rising above the surface of the Earth there corresponds, so to speak, a "negative mountain" formed by the granite masses protruding into the underlying plastic layer of basalt.*

According to Archimedes' law, the mass of a floating

body must be equal to the mass of the displaced material underneath, so that the *presence of an elevation that is in isostatic equilibrium does not signify any actual increase of mass in this region.*

Thus, instead of asking the question: "Why does the mountain not affect the plumb line as much as would correspond to its apparent mass?" we must rather ask: "Why is there any deflection at all?" To answer this last question we must bear in mind that, although the solid crust of the Earth is not strong enough to support the whole mountain, it still possesses sufficient elasticity to prevent the mountain from sinking as deep as it would in the case of a completely plastic substratum. Hence the mountain will be elevated a little higher above the surface than corresponds to complete isostatic equilibrium, and the pendulum suspended alongside it will show a slight deviation from the vertical line. It must also be borne in mind that under the weight of smaller mountains and hills (as well as under "man-made mountains" such as the Egyptian pyramids or the New York skyscrapers) the crust will not bend at all, and the deviation of the plumb line in this case will exactly correspond to the excess of mass above the surface.

The elasticity of the crust also prevents the "negative mountain" from being something like a mirror image of the corresponding elevation above the surface; an imaginary mountain climber making his way through the masses of plastic basalt deep under the Alps will look in vain for anything resembling the upside-down Jungfrau or Matterhorn. Probably all that he will find there is an extensive smooth bulge of granite protruding several kilometres downward into the basaltic layer.

THE RAINS VERSUS THE MOUNTAINS

We have mentioned more than once that those parts of the continental massifs above sea level, especially the high mountains raised by the crumpling of the crust, are subject to the continuous destructive action of water, which pours down on them from the sky during rainy periods and carries large quantities of dissolved and mechanically eroded material into the surrounding seas. We have also said that the amount of salt alone carried to the ocean as the result of the past erosion of continental blocks totals about 20,000,000 cubic kilometres. *If we were able to extract all this salt from the sea and distribute it uniformly over the land surface* of the Earth, it would form a layer 135 metres (about 450 feet) thick. But salt represents only a very small portion of the granite rocks (about 5 per cent), so that *in order to wash out the amount of salt now dissolved in the ocean, rain water has had to erode a granite layer more than 2 kilometres thick!* Whereas the salt extracted from the rocks remains in solution, the other products of erosion, such as sand and gravel, are deposited on the ocean bottom bordering the shore line or on the bottoms of intracontinental seas, forming the steadily growing layer of sedimentary rocks.

The idea that rain water can wash away thousands of feet of continental surface and level the highest mountain ranges will not seem so strange if we bear in mind the enormous periods of time during which this destructive process has been steadily going on.

Direct measurements of the amount of mud carried away by rivers indicate that the surface of the United States alone loses about 800,000,000 tons of its rocky material annually. *Denudation by rain water reduces the* *average height of the continents by 0.02 millimetre per year.** Since Columbus first stepped on the shore of the New World, an outer layer of about 4 inches thick has been carried away into the oceans and seas.

Erosion by rain water is responsible for such peculiar features of the Earth's surface as the Bad Lands of South Dakota (Plate XII), or the deep canyons cut into the solid rock by comparatively unimportant rivers and creeks (Plate XIIIB). Since the surface of the Earth consists of various kinds of rocks with varying resistance to the destructive action of water, the landscape of denuded areas often assumes strange and fantastic shapes. One example is the peculiar structure known as the Devil's Tower, familiar to travellers who have driven through South Dakota along U. S. Highway 9 (Plate XIIIA). Once upon a time this spot was occupied by a magnificent volcano, an outlet for the masses of molten magma from below. Later, the volcanic activity in this region ceased, and the solidified lava filling the volcanic crater formed a long vertical column of basalt. Rain water worked on the dead volcano for centuries upon centuries, and it took hundreds of thousands of years until it finally succeeded in washing away the outer part of the cone formed by the volcanic ashes of numerous eruptions. The remaining tower is merely the original column of solidified lava, and since basalt withstands erosion much better than the softer material of the cone, it will probably take many more hundreds of thousands of years for the rain to obliterate

* The reader must remember that this rate of erosion, corresponding to the present epoch of high mountains, is several times larger than it was during the long submergence stages, when most of the mountains had been already washed away (*cf.* Chapter I, page 4).

completely this last remainder of the ancient volcano.

Since the destruction of mountains by the rapid streams rushing down their steep slopes proceeds considerably faster than the erosion of flatlands, we must expect that *the general effect of the action of rain water will be to obliterate all the characteristic features produced by the crumpling of the crust and transform the continental surfaces into extensive low plains.* It must be noted, however, that to wash away a mountain, rain water must do considerably more work than would seem necessary at first sight. In fact, the process of isostatic adjustment described above operates so that, while the material of the mountain is being carried away by rushing streams, new rocks slowly rise up from below, giving the water additional work to do. *To remove the mountain completely from the surface of the Earth it is necessary, not only to take away its visible protruding part, but also to remove its "roots," which penetrate deep into the crust.* If some ambitious railway company, constructing a new line through a mountainous region, should decide to remove the whole mountain instead of digging a tunnel through it, the advantage obtained by this gigantic construction job would be only temporary, since in a few hundred thousand years a new mountain, of only slightly smaller size, would again rise on the same spot!

Parallel with the permanent upward movement of the mountain regions there goes the slow sinking of those parts of the Earth's surface on which the streams and rivers deposit their loads of eroded material. Since the mountains are raised mainly along the continental shore lines, and since the rain water falling on a mountain runs down both its sides, these sinking regions of the crust must evidently correspond to the oceanic bottoms bordering the continents and to the bottoms of the comparatively shallow seas that are often formed in the lower central portions of the continental massifs. Figure 30 gives a schematic representation of these typical isostatic adjustments of the continents, caused entirely by the activity of rain. As we have said, the deformation of the Earth's crust

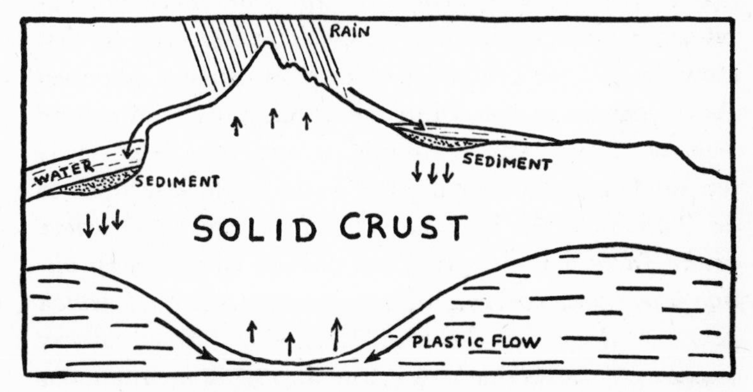

FIGURE 30
The mountain grows anew while being eroded by rain.

resulting from processes of this kind may cause some additional wrinkling of the surface and the formation of local mountain chains.

From the observed rate of denudation it is estimated that *the time necessary for rain waters to obliterate the mountains raised during a revolutionary epoch of mountain formation is several times shorter than the period between two such revolutions.* Hence we must conclude that *the surface of the Earth was quite featureless and flat during most of its history, with many areas completely covered by shallow seas,* and that it is our special privilege to live during one of the comparatively short epochs when the mountains raised by the last revolution are still standing proudly, providing us with beautiful scenery and splendid opportunities for climbing and skiing.

CHAPTER VII

The Evolution of Continents

IS AMERICA DRIFTING AWAY FROM EUROPE?

AS WE have already seen, the large granite blocks comprising the six major continents (Eurasia, Africa, North and South America, Australia, and Antarctica) represent the fragments of the primeval solid crust of the Earth, which was broken up in the process of the Moon's birth. The similarity of the continental shore lines (compare Figure 31) strongly suggests that the general shape of these fragments did not change essentially during the five billion years separating us from the memorable moment of the birth of a daughter to our planet. But, although the western shores of Europe and Africa could be fitted into the eastern shores of North and South America, there are some 4000 miles of Atlantic Ocean separating them today. The continent of Australia also seems to have drifted a considerable distance south-east, leaving room for the waters of the Indian Ocean, while Antarctica has moved due south and is now hidden under a thick sheet of ice. If all this is true, and the similarity of the shore lines is not a mere coincidence, a number of important questions immediately confront us. What kind of forces could have caused the separation of the originally united continental fragments? How long ago did the separation actually take place? Are the distances between the continents still increasing, and should we expect that the continent of North America, drifting farther and farther away from Europe, will sooner or later hit and crush the islands of Japan with its advancing California flank?

The existence of forces acting on continental massifs and attempting to change their relative positions was first recognized by Baron Roland Eötvös, the Hungarian geophysicist, who showed that such forces must necessarily arise as a result of the rotation of the Earth. Remember-

FIGURE 31
Relative position of the fragments of the original crust immediately after the separation of the Moon. (Not to be used as proof of the possibility of invasion of the United States.)

ing that the continents represent masses of comparatively light granite floating on the heavier basaltic layer, we must expect that *they will be acted upon by some kind of centrifugal (or rather "pole-fugal") force, which will try to move them toward the equator.** From the velocity of

* At first sight it might seem that, since the surface of the Earth already possesses the ellipsoidal shape corresponding to its rotation, no such force acting on the floating objects should be available. We must not forget, however, that the centre of gravity of a floating object is *higher* than the centre of gravity of the displaced water would be, and that this difference in height causes the difference in centrifugal force. The phenomenon is somewhat analogous to the effect that can be observed on a steamer floating down a river. In this case (as was first noticed by the airplane designer Anton Fokker on the Maas River near Rotterdam) the steamer is "sliding

the Earth's rotation, it is not difficult to calculate that in the middle latitudes, where the equatorial pull is strongest, the force acting on each square metre of the continental surface is about 50 kilograms. Thus, *the total force acting on Manhattan Island, for example, can be compared with the pull exerted by five thousand trans-atlantic liners as big as the "Queen Elizabeth," tied up to*

FIGURE 32
The equatorial pull on Manhattan Island is comparable to the pull of 5000 liners of the size of the *Queen Elizabeth* tied up to the embankment of Battery Park and sailing full steam southward.

the shore along the Battery Park embankment and steaming southward at full speed (Figure 32).

It is evident that when the continents were still floating on the ocean of molten basalt, these forces of equatorial pull were able to move them slowly across the molten surface in an endeavour to distribute them uniformly along the equator. The motion produced by these forces must necessarily have been very complicated, owing to the irregular shape of the fragments; no attempt has been made as yet to reconstruct the spreading-out process of the con-

down the water," and thus moves somewhat faster than the river itself in spite of the fact that its propellers are not turning.

tinents on the basis of theoretical considerations. It is clear, however, that *the first effect of these forces must have been to separate the fragmented pieces of the crust from one another, and to enlarge the cracks already existing between them.* If the equatorial pull had had its way and been able to finish its work, the geography of our globe would represent a rather peculiar picture. The large Pacific hole, which resulted from the separation of the Moon,

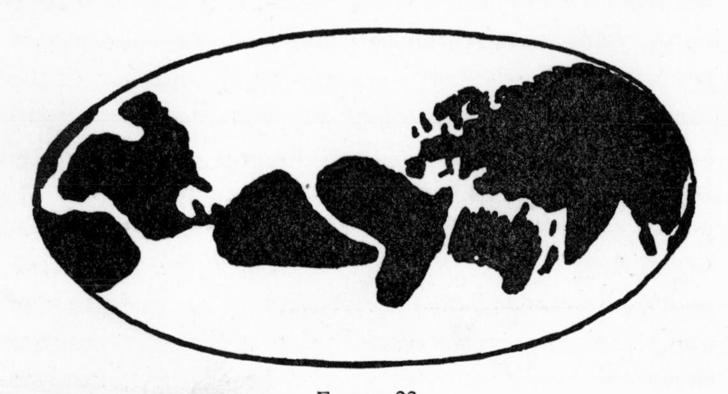

FIGURE 33
This is how the map of world might look today if the separation of continents had not been stopped by the freezing of the basalt ocean.

would have disappeared completely and the continental massifs would form an almost continuous equatorial belt, with two large circular oceans in the Northern and Southern Hemispheres (Figure 33). The fact that the map of the world does not look quite like that today proves that *something prevented the equatorial pull from finishing its work;* it is most natural to assume that the drifting process had been slowed down and stopped before reaching its ultimate goal by the increasing resistance of the rapidly solidifying surface of the basalt ocean. We have seen that the surface of the molten Earth could have remained in the molten state for only a few thousand years before being covered with a thin but quickly growing layer of solid crust. In the case of the freshly opened surface of molten basalt, exposed to the cold of interplanetary space, the solidification must have taken place considerably more rapidly, because the material of the outer parts of our planets must already have been rather viscous as the result of previous cooling. Because of this increasing viscosity the continental drift could not have been very fast from the beginning, while the rapid formation of the basalt crust (now constituting the bottoms of the oceans) must have stopped it in the same way as the growing layer of ice maroons a polar exploration ship at the approach of winter. It must be borne in mind that, according to these views, *the drift of the continents must have ceased at a comparatively early stage of the evolution of our planet;* and we can hardly expect that any essential changes in their relative position took place after the ocean basins became sufficiently cool to be filled with water. The "continental drift hypothesis," in its original form as proposed by the German geophysicist Alfred Wegener, assumed that the motion of the continents continued throughout the later geological epochs; Eurasia, Africa, and both the Americas were considered to have been close neighbours as late as the Carboniferous period.* This supposition, which was developed chiefly to explain the similarity of the flora and fauna of these continents through the migration of plants and animals while they were in direct contact, hardly stands up in the light of our present knowledge. In fact, it can be easily calculated that the

* I.e., 200,000,000 years ago.

equatorial pull acting on an average-sized continent situated in the middle latitudes is several thousand times smaller than the resistance of the basaltic layer forming the underlying bottom of the ocean along its southern shores. It is true, of course, that during earlier geologic periods the thickness of the ocean bottoms was somewhat smaller than it is now and that the drift forces were somewhat larger, owing to the more rapid rotation of the Earth.* However, it hardly seems possible that any noticeable effect of the drift forces could have been manifested, even with these corrections, during the periods following the solidification of the crust.

From the above considerations it also follows *a fortiori* that *no change of the relative positions of the continents should be expected at the present time.* Some time ago, much attention was attracted by observations indicating that the distance between Greenland and Europe had apparently increased by about 32 metres during a period of 33 years (from 1873 to 1907). But since recent and more careful observations (1927 to 1936) have failed to show even a small fraction of the previously announced drift, we must conclude that the older results were probably due to insufficiently exact methods of measurement and that no such drift actually exists.

RECONSTRUCTING THE "BOOK OF SEDIMENTS"

Although the general shape and the relative position of the continental massifs could not have changed much since the solidification of the ocean basins, the surface features of the continents have been undergoing continuous transformation owing to the combined action of the moun-

* See Chapter III.

tain-raising forces and the destructive action of rain. This periodic formation of mountain chains and their subsequent destruction by water are clearly shown by the character of the deposits of eroded material carried into the seas by the rivers of the past. In fact, the nature of such deposits depends to a large extent on the character of the surface that is being eroded.

During the revolutionary periods, such as the one that we are living in now, high mountains rise everywhere on the surface of the continents, and erosion proceeds very fast. Rapid streams rushing down steep mountain slopes break off comparatively large pieces of rock by purely mechanical action, and the deposits formed during these periods consist mainly of rather rough materials, such as gravel and coarse sand. On the other hand, during the long inter-revolutionary epochs, when most of the mountains are already washed away completely, and the surface of the continents is level and dull, the process of erosion necessarily slows down. There are no rushing mountain streams, no noisy waterfalls, and the rain water that continues to fall on the Earth's surface is drained into the oceans and seas by broad, slow rivers running across low, almost horizontal plains. During these long periods, chemical erosion is more effective than purely mechanical disintegration.

Water, slowly moving across the surface of the Earth, carries into solution various soluble parts of the rocks, leaving fine sand and clay as the residue. The dissolved material is mostly calcium carbonate, which is carried out into the seas and deposited as thick layers of limestone.

Thus, if we were able to examine some spots on the Earth where the formation of sedimentary deposits has been going on uninterruptedly throughout the geologic history of our planet, a cross-section of the deposits would look very regular. We would find periodic repetitions of fine and coarse material, corresponding to the revolutionary and inter-revolutionary epochs, and we would be able to reconstruct the entire history of our planet chapter by chapter. Such a complete edition of the "Book of Sediments" undoubtedly exists on the bottoms of the oceans along the continental shore lines, since, being continuously submerged, these areas have been receiving an uninterrupted flow of eroded material from the near-by lands. Unfortunately, however, these submerged pages of the Earth's history are quite inaccessible to the hammer of the geologist at present, and we must content ourselves with the study of the deposits formed in the intracontinental shallow seas and brought up to the surface of the Earth by the subsequent elevation of the ground and the erosion of the layers lying above.

Since the surface of the continents has been moving up and down irregularly throughout the Earth's history, and the interior seas have always been changing their sites, the records contained in the sediments left at any one place are necessarily incomplete. In Figure 34 we give a schematic picture of what we can expect to find at a spot that was subject to three submergences, but now is on dry land. Let us suppose that during the first submergence period the deposits carried down by the rivers formed six successive layers, which we distinguish by the numbers 1 to 6.* Suppose now that after these layers, representing a continuous record of the corresponding interval of the Earth's

* The enumeration of the layers used here does not correspond to any real division of geologic time and is used only for convenience in discussion.

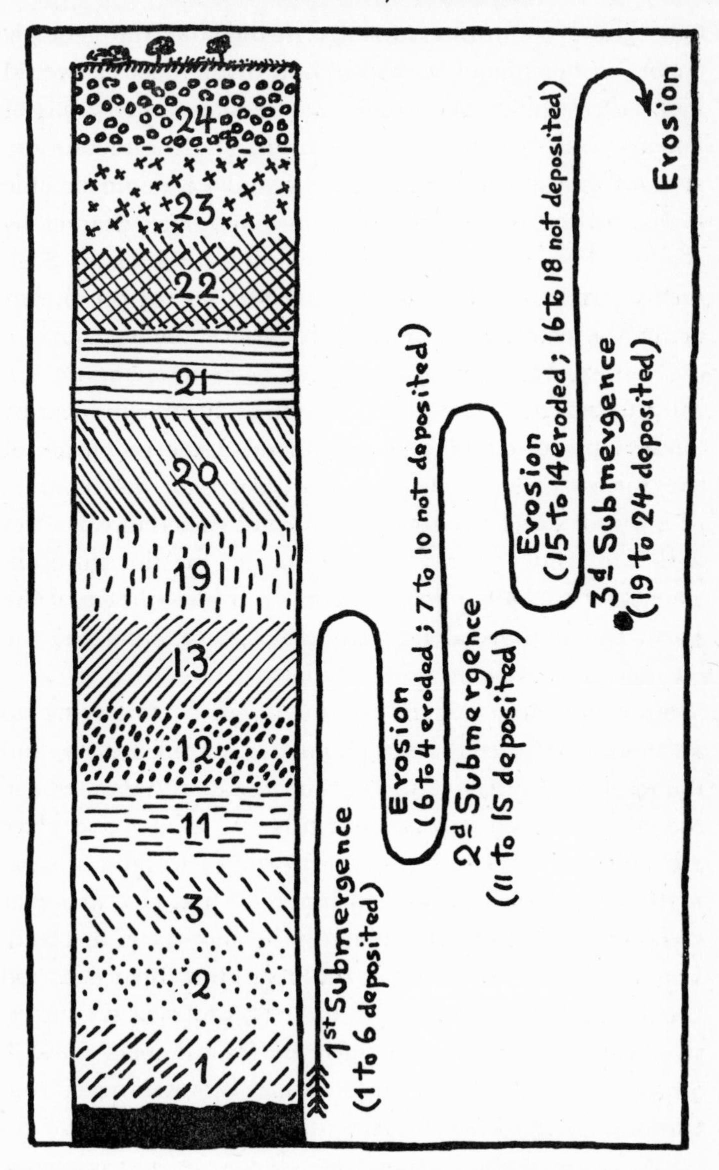

FIGURE 34
Showing how the periodic elevations of the ground spoil the continuity of geologic records.

history, were formed, movements of the crust elevated this particular locality above sea level, so that the newly formed layers were exposed to the destructive action of rain water. During the period of elevation part of the sedimentary layers was carried away by erosion, and this material, mixed with material taken from other places, was deposited elsewhere. While new sedimentary layers (let us say 7, 8, 9, and 10) were being formed on the bottom of the ocean, where the deposits were accumulating continuously, our locality was only losing its material, the three upper layers (6, 5, and 4) being completely removed. Thus, when the new submergence occurred, layer 11 began to be deposited directly on top of old layer 3.

Inspecting Figure 34 further we find that the only sedimentary layers left in this hypothetical locality and presenting themselves to the hammer of the geologist are those numbered 1, 2, 3, 11, 12, 13, 19, 20, 21, 22, 23, 24, while all the others were never formed or were eroded by rain water.

But though the layers deposited in any given locality represent only a collection of disunited occasional pages of the "Book of Sediments," we can try to reconstruct the complete copy of the book by comparing the findings in a number of places that were submerged at different times. This task is, of course, a very difficult one, and work in this field represents the main subject of historical geology. The principal method used in the reconstruction of the complete "geological column" from the disunited fragments is based on the "principle of overlapping" explained schematically in Figure 35. It may happen that, comparing two separate fragments corresponding to the uninterrupted sedimentation process in different localities, we notice that the upper layers of one fragment are of the same nature as the lower layers of another. If such is the

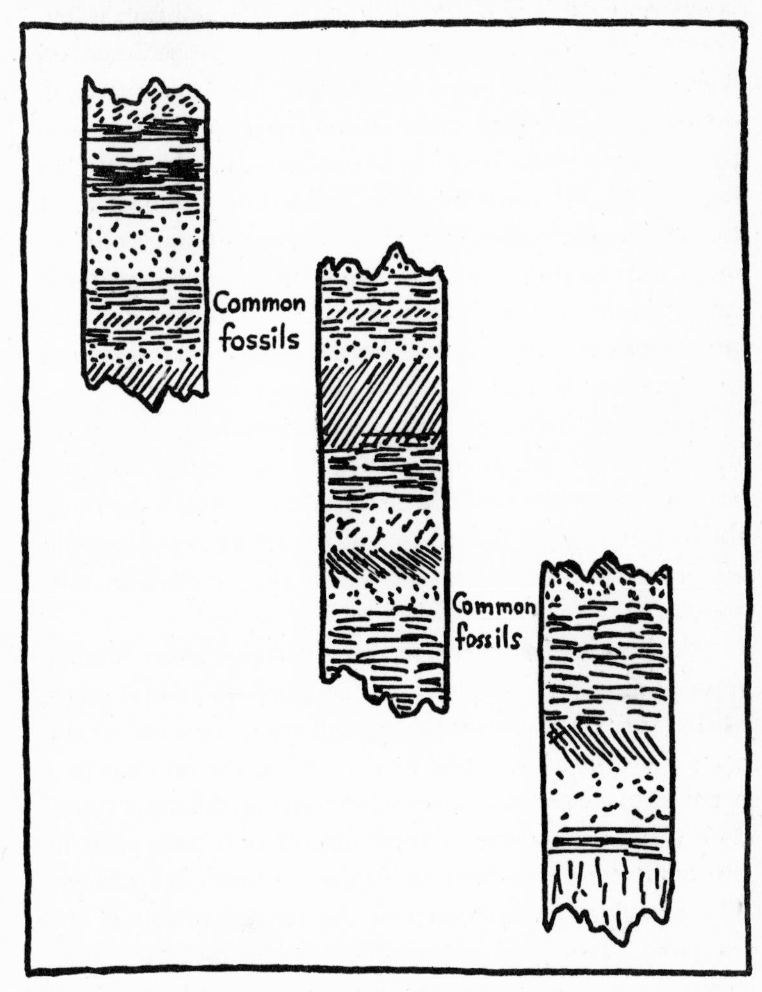

FIGURE 35
Putting together disconnected fragments of the "Book of Sediments."

case, the conclusion is inevitable that the layers at the top of the first fragment were being formed simultaneously with the bottom layers of the second; putting the two fragments together so that the layers corresponding to the same time overlap, we get a continuous record covering the larger time interval.*

It must be borne in mind, however, that since the differences between purely physical and chemical characteristics of various deposits are not very large, and since the same kinds of deposits repeat periodically in time, the method of overlapping described above would not yield much in the way of results if the sedimentary layer did not contain the fossilized remainders of different plants and animals living during the corresponding epochs. In fact, the development of historical geology is inseparably connected with the development of palæontology (i.e., the science of ancient life); together with the complete geological column representing the history of land and sea we also get the complete record of the evolution of life.

* A similar method of overlapping is very successfully used in studying prehistoric Indian villages in different parts of North America. Since such villages were mostly situated on the lake shore, one finds at the bottoms of these lakes a large number of petrified logs that once formed the village buildings. Now, it is known that the pattern of vegetation rings in the cross-section of a tree trunk is just as characteristic of the time interval during which the tree was growing as the fingerprint of a man, and depends upon the climatic conditions during the life span of the tree. In fact, during warm summers with plenty of rain the corresponding annual rings will grow thicker, whereas very thin rings will correspond to dry summers. Thus, if one finds two logs in which the patterns of annual rings partly overlap, one can be sure that the two trees were growing at the same time (corresponding to the period of overlap). Putting together a large number of logs, selected in such a way that the outer rings of each (i.e., the rings formed shortly before the tree was cut down) coincide with more central rings on the next one, it is possible to build a continuous "tree column" covering an interval of many centuries. From this column we can get exact information as to the dates when different logs were cut down for construction purposes. What is most interesting, we can also get a rough meteorological record of the climatic changes in this particular locality over a period of time during which the word "meteorology" itself was unknown.

The work of collecting the fragmentary pages of the Earth's history here and there and binding them together into one consistent volume must, of course, become increasingly difficult as we go back to more and more remote epochs. Thus, while the later parts of the "Book of Sediments" are fairly complete by now, the records of earlier periods are still in a very imperfect state. Classification of these early pages of the book becomes particularly difficult because at the time they were "written" life on the Earth either did not exist at all or was limited to the simplest organisms, which left no trace in the sediments of that time.

The completed "Book of Sediments" still possessed one essential defect: it completely lacked any chronology, and though we could say that one layer was formed after or before another, we had no idea of the period of time separating them. In order to get the "timing" of geological events, very elaborate but uncertain speculations about the deposition rates of different types of materials had always been necessary, and it is therefore very fortunate that the discovery of radioactivity gave us a much simpler and much more exact method of establishing a geologic time scale.

In Chapter I we described in some detail how a fairly good idea of the time when different igneous rocks solidified is obtained by studying the relative amounts of the disintegration products of uranium and thorium contained in them. Applying this method to the rocks formed by volcanic eruptions in the past and found now and then in different sedimentary layers, we can add the last touch to the "Book of Sediments" by marking on each page the approximate date at which it was "written."

CHAPTERS AND PARAGRAPHS OF THE "BOOK OF SEDIMENTS"

The "Book of Sediments," as reconstructed by the work of generations of geologists, certainly represents a most extensive historic document, alongside which all the thick volumes of the history of the human race are no more than an insignificant booklet. As we have seen, the layer eroded from continental surfaces by rain water is, on the average, some 2 kilometres thick. Since, however, these disintegration products are mostly deposited in comparatively small areas along the shores, the actual thickness of the geologic column is considerably greater. Putting together all the fragmented pieces of this column we obtain a total thickness of about 100 kilometres, each year corresponding to a layer about 0.1 millimetre thick. *If we consider a year's deposit as one "page" of the "Book of Sediments," such a page will be comparable in thickness with a page in any ordinary book. The reconstructed part of the "book" will have about one billion pages, covering the same number of years of the Earth's history.* This thickness, however, corresponds only to the later part of the evolution of the surface of our planet, and there probably are millions of earlier fragmented pages, most of which still lie hidden under the surface. Pursuing our analogy with the ordinary book, we must bear in mind, of course, that one page of the "Earth book" does not record much of its history, and that in order to notice any changes one must thumb through at least several hundred thousand pages. This is also true of the book of human history; whereas the year-to-year changes may have been of special interest to the persons living during these epochs, considerably longer periods of time are needed to manifest any interesting changes in the evolution of humanity.

The first important feature of the "Book of Sediments" is that, like any other book, it is divided into a number of separate chapters corresponding to the revolutionary epochs and the intermediate long periods of submergence discussed above. It is very hard to say how many chapters there are in the "book," since its earliest parts are still in a very fragmentary and incomplete state; only the last three chapters covering the last 500,000,000 years tell a more or less complete and consistent story. Since, however, these last three chapters represent about one-quarter of the total life span of our planet, we must conclude that the "book" has a total of twelve chapters. This is in fairly close accord with the probable number of revolutionary periods caused by the cooling of the Earth. The last three chapters of the "book," however, are of particular interest, since, as indicated above, they cover practically the entire period during which life has existed on our planet. The three periods of time described in these last three chapters are known as the *Early Palæozoic, Late Palæozoic,* and *Mesozoic* eras of the Earth's history. Finally, at the very end of the "book" we find the beginning of the new *Cainozoic* chapter, which commenced just recently. In geologic language the expression "just recently" means "about forty million years ago" and is completely justified by the fact that this period of time is very short indeed, compared with the average length of each chapter, which covers between one and two hundred million years. Besides the natural division of the Earth's history into a number of chapters, each starting with a revolutionary epoch of mountain formation, geologists

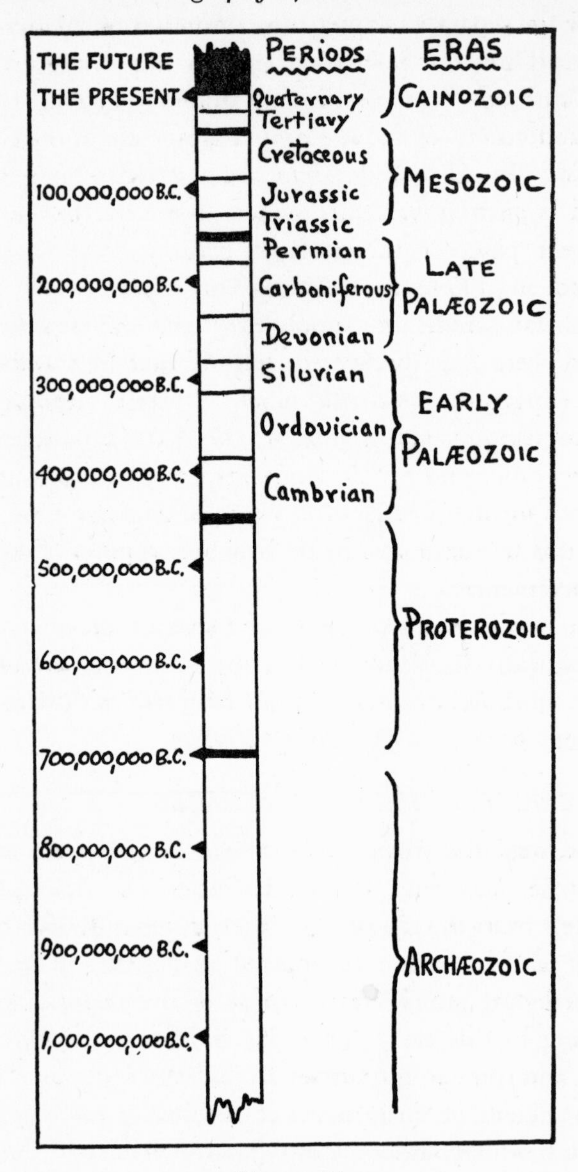

FIGURE 36
Divisions of geologic time.

divide the separate chapter into a number of smaller paragraphs. Thus, the Early Palæozoic chapter is divided into the *Cambrian, Ordovician,* and *Silurian* periods, whereas the subdivisions of the Mesozoic chapter are known as the *Triassic, Jurassic,* and *Cretaceous* periods. Such subdivision is entirely arbitrary and is based on the fact that different parts of the geologic column were originally studied in different localities. For example, the name "Cambrian" indicates simply that the deposits of that period were first discovered and studied in Cambridgeshire (England), while the name "Jurassic" similarly refers to deposits first found in the Jura Mountains between France and Switzerland. Since there are no natural grounds for the further subdivision of geologic time, however, this terminology can be retained simply for the sake of convenience.

The division of geologic time discussed above is shown schematically in Figure 36; in the following sections we give a short account of the major happenings during these different periods of the Earth's history.

THE EARLIEST FRAGMENTED PAGES

The very first pages of the "Book of Sediments" must, of course, date back to the day when the first drop of rain fell from the sky on the slowly cooling surface of our planet, and the first crack started its destructive work on the primeval granite crust. Most of the deposits corresponding to this early epoch are hidden deep under the Earth and come to the surface in but very few places. They consist chiefly of thick sheets of *micaschists* and *dolomitic marbles,* which under careful microscopic and chemical analysis prove to be ordinary sandstones and limestones greatly compressed and "metamorphized" by exceedingly high pressures and temperatures at the great depths to which they were thrust by the weight of the later sediments formed above them. These primeval sedimentary layers are sometimes well over 100,000 feet thick, indicating that their formation must have taken place at least several hundred million years ago, that is, quite a large fraction of the Earth's total life span. It is of interest to note that, unlike later deposits, these early sediments contain but little salt, indicating that sea water must have been quite fresh at that time. As the salinity of sea and ocean water has been steadily increasing ever since the oceans first appeared (see Chapter I), we must conclude that the formation of these deposits coincided approximately with the time when the ocean basins first filled up, and that in this sense they really represent the very first deposits of eroded material ever formed on the surface of the Earth.

This first extensive period of sedimentation was evidently followed by the revolutionary crumpling of the Earth's crust known as the *Laurentian revolution,** during which large masses of molten granite were poured over these layers, while the layers themselves were uplifted and folded into giant mountains.† It is useless, of course, to look for these mountains on present-day geographical maps, for they were completely obliterated by the action

* It must be remembered that this revolution need not have been the first one to take place on the surface of the Earth. In fact, there probably were several earlier outbursts of tectonic activity, but since the "Book of Sediments" was not yet in existence at the time, we have no way of judging them.

† As was mentioned in Chapter III, the fact that the volcanic eruptions of that time were ejecting masses of molten granite (not basalt!) indicates that the solid crust of the Earth then was considerably thinner than it is now, so that part of granite was still in a molten state.

of rain water many hundreds of millions of years ago. Since the deposits of that distant past can now be found in but few places on the surface of the Earth (for example, in eastern Canada), it is altogether impossible to form any idea of the geographical distribution of these early mountains from their remaining roots. The study of radioactivity in the granite layers formed during this first recorded revolution indicates that their age is only somewhat less than one billion years, which gives us the approximate date when the first sedimentation period ended.

After the erosion of the first recorded mountain chains, large areas of the continents were again covered by water, and thick layers of new deposits were formed on top of the previous ones. Then another revolution (the *Algomian*) ensued, accompanied by new mountain-formation processes and new intrusions of granite lavas, again followed by a long quiet sedimentation period. Then again a revolution and still another sedimentation. . . .

But the reader is probably growing tired of this constant repetition of the words "revolution" and "sedimentation"; to cheer him up we can tell him that there will be some more colour to the picture after one more repetition. In fact, beginning with the fifth recorded revolution, known as the *Charnian*, we leave the dark prehistoric periods of the Earth's life and enter the epoch comparable to that of ancient Egypt in the history of humanity. The sedimentary layers formed during the epochs following the Charnian revolution have been studied in many places on the Earth; they give us a rather complete picture of the evolution of its surface. Besides, they begin to contain the fossils of different primitive animals in steadily increasing numbers, which is of great help in establishing the "page sequence" in the book of the Earth's history. The deposits formed after the Charnian revolution represent three complete chapters of the "Book of Sediments," and on top of them we find the comparatively thin layers constituting the beginning of the latest chapter, in the writing of which we have the pleasure of participating ourselves.

THREE COMPLETE CHAPTERS OF THE "BOOK OF SEDIMENTS"

As a result of the Charnian revolution, which opens the historical era of the Earth's history, all the continents were lifted high above sea level, and they were probably considerably larger in extent than they are today. In North America, for example, this general uplift caused the Atlantic and the Pacific to recede so that dry land extended many hundreds of miles into the regions now covered by the oceans. The present basins of the Gulf of Mexico and the Caribbean Sea were also occupied by land, while both the Americas, now united only by a narrow isthmus, formed one continuous continent, as indicated in the first map of our cinematographic history of North America (Figure 38 on page 156). On the other side of the Atlantic the continents also protruded much farther west than they do now; in particular a long string of land known as "Atlantida"* reached out from the British Isles toward Greenland.

But, as after all the previous revolutions, the uplifted continents slowly began to sink back into the plastic mass below, and the incessant pounding of the rain washed away the rocky material of the mountains and high

* This land, of course, has nothing to do with the mythical "Atlantis" of the ancients, since it existed hundreds of millions of years before man appeared on the surface of the Earth.

plateaux. Ocean water crept inland and, covering the lower parts of continents, formed numerous inland seas. On the continent of Eurasia, the waters of the ocean, penetrating deep into the interior, formed an extensive inland basin covering all the area now occupied by Germany, southern Russia, the southern part of Siberia, and most of China. This large inland sea was surrounded by a ring of highlands passing through the present positions of Scotland, Scandinavia, northern Siberia, the Himalayas, the Caucasus, the Balkans, and the Alps.* The continent of Africa, however, seems to have been completely out of the water during all that time, and it was connected with Europe by dry land extending over the present Mediterranean basin. The northern part of Australia was submerged by the waters of the Indian Ocean, whereas its southern part extended much farther south toward the Antarctic. On this side of the Atlantic, the advance of the ocean in the equatorial region almost split the American continent in two (North and South America), and much of what is now Mexico and Texas was also inundated. The waters of the North Pacific covered most of the central area of North America, including the entire Mississippi Valley, the region of the Great Lakes, and part of southern Canada. South of the equator, the advancing Atlantic waters formed an extensive shallow sea covering most of what is now Brazil.

Although this extensive inundation was the most characteristic feature of the Early Palæozoic chapter of the Earth's history and lasted for about 160 million years, one must not think that this epoch was completely devoid of

* It must be remembered that these elevations were completely obliterated long ago by erosion; the mountains now rising in these regions are of considerably later formation (see page 153 of this chapter).

movements of the crust. There are, in fact, some traces of minor mountain-formation activity, and the slow elevations and sinkings taking place in the continental areas were causing the inland seas to change the shape of their shore lines continuously. But all these changes were on a minor scale, and the stresses in the crust resulting from the cooling of the Earth were only slowly gathering their forces for the major outbreak that finally took place in the year 280,000,000 B.C.

The great disturbances of the Earth's crust that opened the next, the Late Palæozoic, chapter of the "'Book of Sediments" are known as the *Caledonian revolution,* the name being derived from the mountains of the same name in Scotland and northern Ireland, where the results of the revolution were particularly pronounced. As the result of this revolution, a large mountain chain was elevated along a line running through Scotland, the North Sea, and the Scandinavian peninsula up to Spitsbergen.

The extension of this chain ran across northern Siberia and formed the elevated northern border of the Asiatic continent. Another mountain chain extended from Scotland through the North Atlantic all the way to Greenland, completely separating the Arctic Ocean from the waters of the North Atlantic. In North America, where the revolutionary activity began somewhat later than in Eurasia, high mountain ranges were raised along a line running from the eastern extremity of Canada through Nova Scotia and continuing farther south along the Atlantic coast. There was also very pronounced activity at many points in South America, South Africa, and Australia, as can be seen from the map of Figure 37, which shows the major accomplishments of the Caledonian revolution.

In spite of all this large-scale mountain-folding activity, the Caledonian revolution apparently was far from being as intensive as the previous one, and the general upheaval of land was considerably less pronounced. In fact, whereas the waters were completely forced away from the continental surfaces during the Charnian revolution, the Cale-

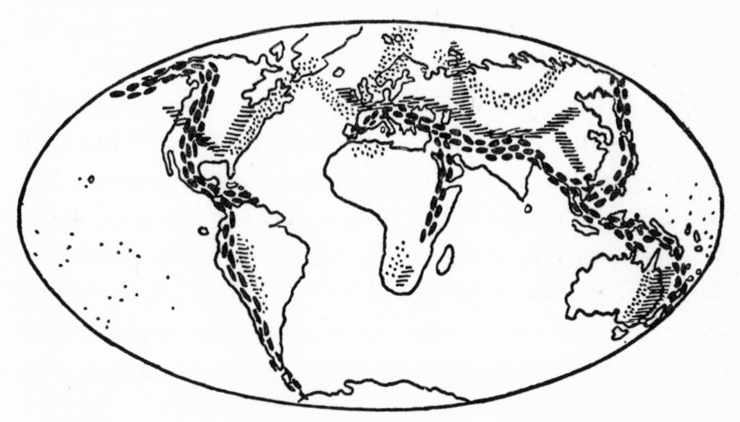

FIGURE 37

Three great mountain-folding revolutions of the last 300,000,000 years.
1. Mountain chains of the Caledonian revolution (about 300,000,000 B.C.) represented by small dots.
2. Mountain chains of the Appalachian revolution (about 150,000,000 B.C.) represented by thin lines.
3. Mountain chains of the Cainozoic revolution (about 4,000,000 B.C.) represented by large dots.

donian uplift left the Central North American Sea almost untouched, together with the large water basin of Central and Eastern Europe. Another indication of the comparative mildness of the Caledonian revolution is the fact that it evidently did not relieve the stress in the Earth's crust entirely, since we find rather pronounced activity of the crust through the entire Late Palæozoic chapter. There were countless small elevations and sinkings of land and the formation of various small mountain chains throughout the 130 million years that separated the Caledonian from the subsequent Appalachian revolution.

This revolution, which opens the Mesozoic chapter, culminated the crust movements that had been continuing on a minor scale all through the previous period of submergence and raised a number of high mountain chains all over the world (Figure 37).

In North America, the folding of the crust formed a V-shaped mountain system with its apex in Texas. One branch of this system extended along the Gulf Coast and all along the present site of the Appalachian Mountains, while another branch ran north-west, forming the ancestral Rockies and extending all the way to Puget Sound. In Europe, the compression of the crust formed a long chain beginning somewhere in Ireland (or farther out in the Atlantic), running through central France and southern Germany, and probably joining the Asiatic mountain chain north of the present site of the Himalayas.

Like all the other mountains of the past, these once magnificent chains were long ago obliterated by rain, and the fact that some of them are at present slightly elevated above the continental plains is due to much later upheavals. The present Appalachians, from which the name of the revolution itself is derived, and the Vosges and Sudeten Mountains, which came into prominence in connexion with events of the Hitler regime, represent but poor reminders of the glory of the year 150,000,000 B.C.

The Mesozoic submergence period, lasting down to the most recent revolution, which took place only 40 million years ago, is in many respects analogous to the previous periods of submergence. Countless lowlands, marshes, and shallow seas provided vast playgrounds for the giant lizards that dominated the animal world of that time.

But the stresses in the crust were gathering new strength, and the Earth was preparing for its latest revolution, which gave its surface its present aspect.

THE BEGINNING OF THE MOST RECENT CHAPTER

As we have said, the latest revolution, known as the Cainozoic, began about 40 million years ago; according to all indications, it is still going on at the present time. The fact that we live in a revolutionary period should not lead us to expect to see new mountains rising from the Earth every day like mushrooms! As we have seen above, all the processes in the Earth's crust take place extremely slowly, and it is quite possible that all the earthquakes and volcanic activity occurring throughout the recorded history of the human race represent preparations for the next major catastrophe, which will result in the formation of new chains in some unexpected place. The evidence forcing us to assume that the activities of the Cainozoic revolution are still far from concluded is based on the fact that everything accomplished by this latest revolution up to now (i.e., the Rockies, the Alps, the Andes, the Himalayas, etc.) is still considerably short of the achievements of any of the previous ones. Though "our" revolution may simply be not so world-shaking as past revolutions were, it seems more reasonable to assume merely that it has not reached its peak as yet, and that we are now living during one of the relative lulls in activity.

Nearly all the mountains now existing on the surface of the Earth were raised up by this last revolution, and if our conclusion that this revolution is not yet completed is true, more mountain chains are bound to be formed in the "immediate future" (in the geological sense of the word, of course).

The last 40 million years, representing the beginning of the Cainozoic chapter, is arbitrarily divided into six consecutive paragraphs known as: Palæocene, Eocene, Oligocene, Miocene, Pliocene, and Pleistocene periods.* The latest of these periods began in the great epoch of glaciation that we shall discuss in the next chapter, and it continues down to the present time.

One of the first great achievements of the Cainozoic revolution (Figure 37) was the giant crumpling of the crust in the southern part of Asia, which raised the brand-new mountains of the Himalayas high above the surrounding plains. This crumpling was accompanied by terrific volcanic activity, and unprecedented quantities of basaltic lava were spread over the surrounding regions. The Deccan plateau, for example, which includes a large part of the Indian peninsula, rests upon basaltic rocks 10,000 feet thick, the cooled-down lava poured over the surface of the Earth during this period of upheaval.

Another giant eruption of subterranean material also occurred in Japan at about the same time.

On this side of the Atlantic, the compression of the crust during the early part of the Cainozoic revolution (in the Palæocene period) raised a giant mountain chain running almost from pole to pole and now known as the Rockies in North America and the Andes south of the equator. The folding of the major American mountain system was also accompanied by volcanic activity, second

* The first five periods are often united under the general name of "Tertiary" and the latest one is then called the "Quaternary" period. In some classifications the Palæocene epoch is included in the Mesozoic era.

only to the Indian instance mentioned above; the layers erupted lava, some places several thousand feet deep, and formed the extensive Columbia plateau in the states of Washington and Oregon.

These great events of the "first days" of the revolution evidently relieved the stress in the crust somewhat, and the Eocene and Oligocene periods were characterized by comparative quiescence and the lowering of the land elevated previously. But during the following Miocene period, only about 20 million years after the first outbreak, the revolutionary activity was resumed. The land was again elevated considerably, pushing back the ocean waters that had managed to creep up on it during the period of quiescence, and new mountain folds, including the Alps in Europe and the Cascade Range in North America, were formed on the surface of our planet. This second outburst of the revolution continued on a somewhat smaller scale during the subsequent Pliocene period, and is still continuing at the present time. Whether the Miocene outburst was really the final one of this revolution we do not know, but, as we have indicated above, it is likely that our present comparatively quiet epoch is merely a short breathing spell before the next outburst of revolutionary activity.

CINEMATOGRAPHIC HISTORY OF NORTH AMERICA

In the foregoing sections we gave a brief abstract of the history of the continents as it can be read in the "Book of Sediments." Naturally enough, we had to confine ourselves to the general features of the revolutionary epochs and the intervening periods of slow decay and submergence that permit the division of the "book" into well-

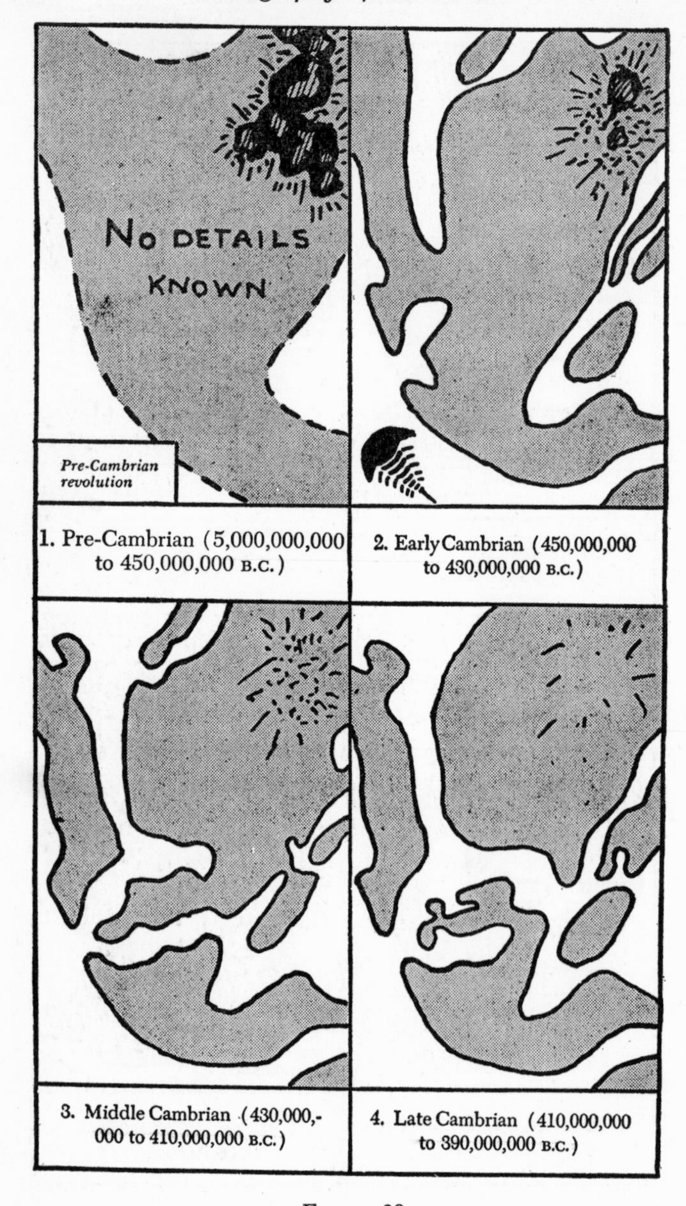
No details known
Pre-Cambrian revolution
1. Pre-Cambrian (5,000,000,000 to 450,000,000 B.C.)
2. Early Cambrian (450,000,000 to 430,000,000 B.C.)
3. Middle Cambrian (430,000,-000 to 410,000,000 B.C.)
4. Late Cambrian (410,000,000 to 390,000,000 B.C.)

Figure 38

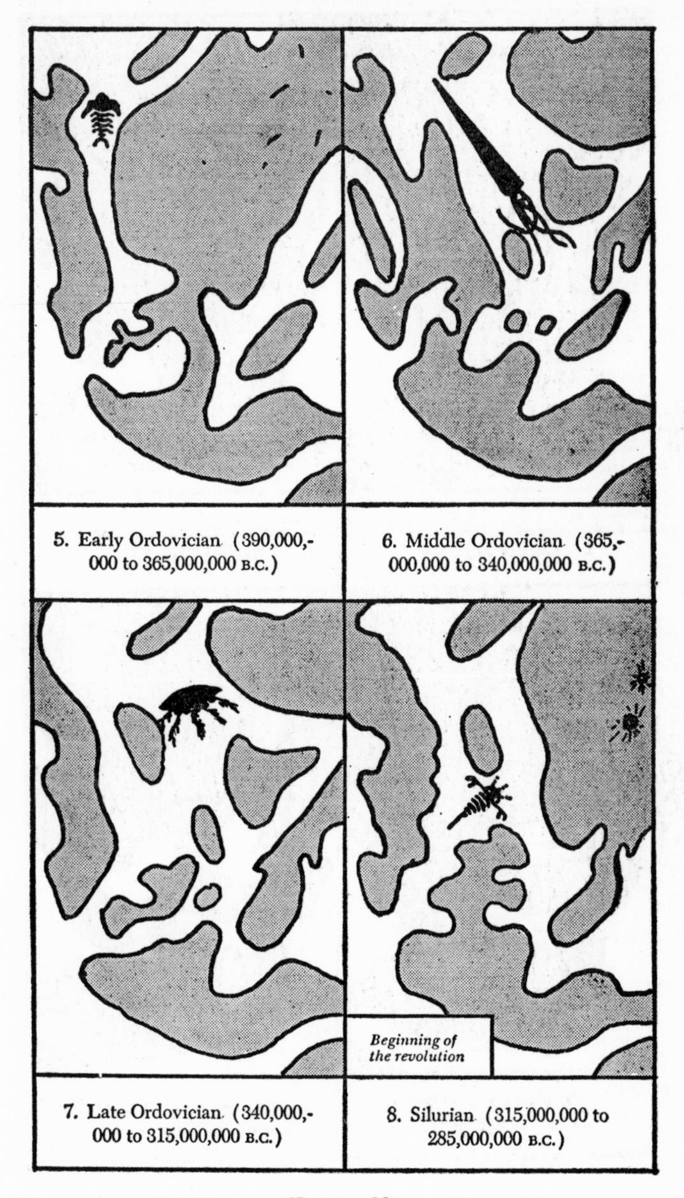

5. Early Ordovician (390,000,000 to 365,000,000 B.C.)

6. Middle Ordovician (365,000,000 to 340,000,000 B.C.)

7. Late Ordovician (340,000,000 to 315,000,000 B.C.)

8. Silurian (315,000,000 to 285,000,000 B.C.)

FIGURE 39

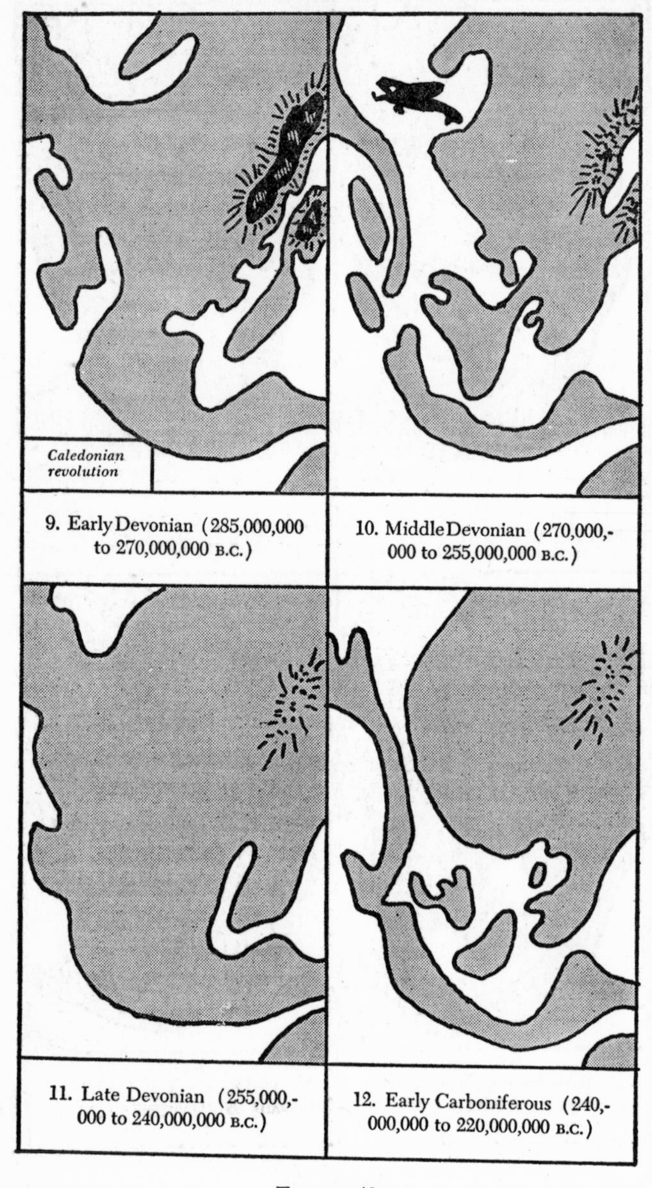
Caledonian
revolution
9. Early Devonian (285,000,000 to 270,000,000 B.C.)
10. Middle Devonian (270,000,000 to 255,000,000 B.C.)
11. Late Devonian (255,000,000 to 240,000,000 B.C.)
12. Early Carboniferous (240,000,000 to 220,000,000 B.C.)

FIGURE 40

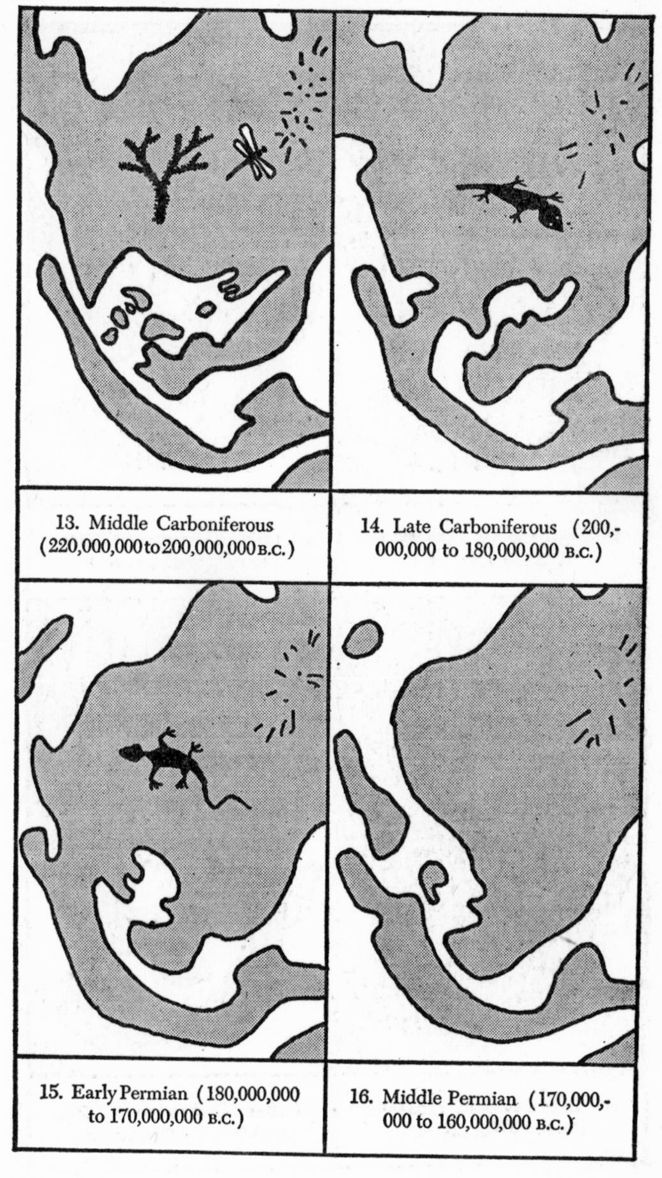

13. Middle Carboniferous (220,000,000 to 200,000,000 B.C.)

14. Late Carboniferous (200,000,000 to 180,000,000 B.C.)

15. Early Permian (180,000,000 to 170,000,000 B.C.)

16. Middle Permian (170,000,000 to 160,000,000 B.C.)

FIGURE 41

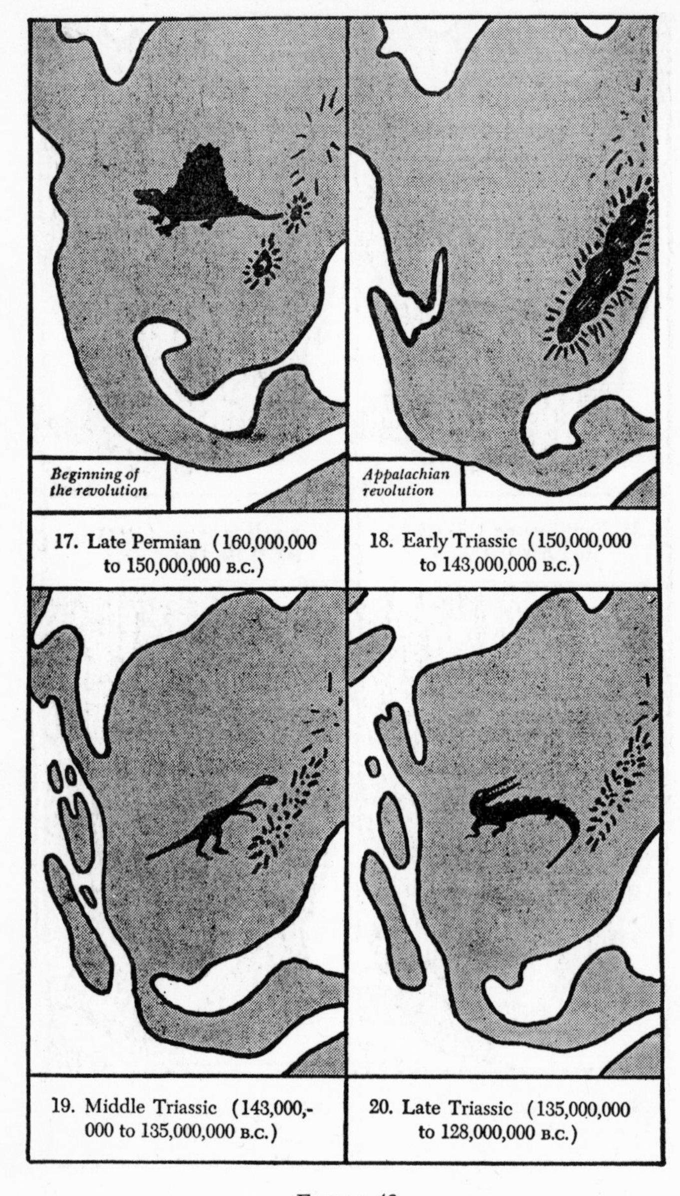
Beginning of the revolution
Appalachian revolution
17. Late Permian (160,000,000 to 150,000,000 B.C.)
18. Early Triassic (150,000,000 to 143,000,000 B.C.)
19. Middle Triassic (143,000,-000 to 135,000,000 B.C.)
20. Late Triassic (135,000,000 to 128,000,000 B.C.)

FIGURE 42

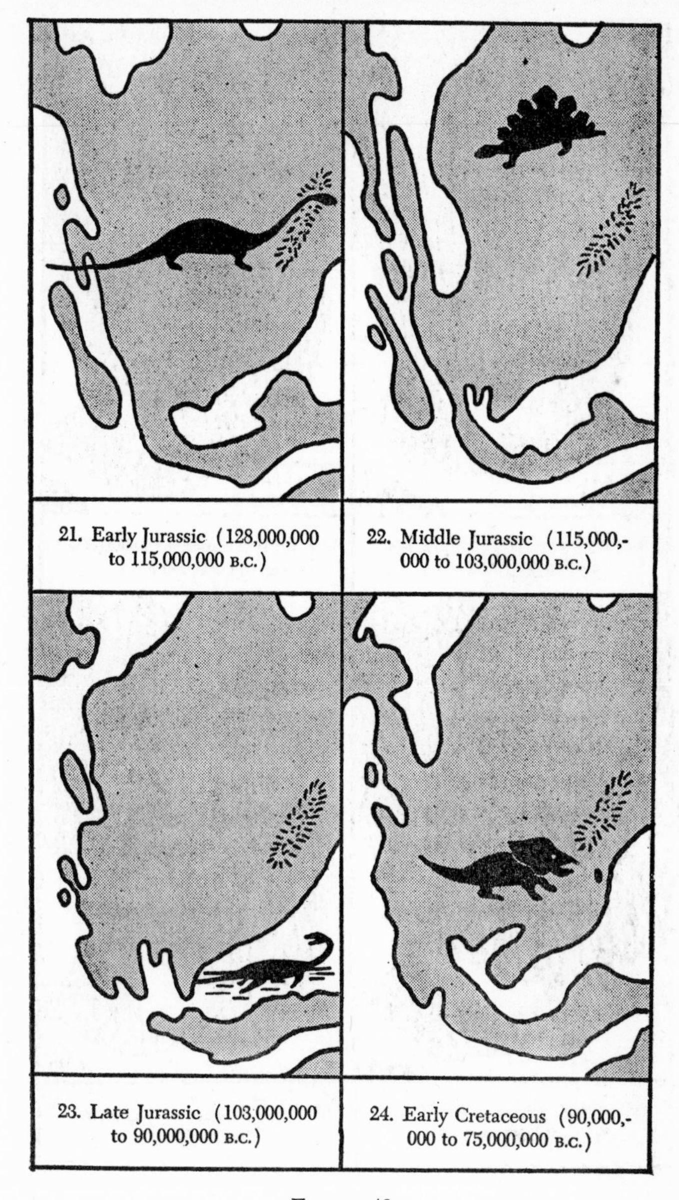

21. Early Jurassic (128,000,000 to 115,000,000 B.C.)

22. Middle Jurassic (115,000,000 to 103,000,000 B.C.)

23. Late Jurassic (103,000,000 to 90,000,000 B.C.)

24. Early Cretaceous (90,000,000 to 75,000,000 B.C.)

FIGURE 43

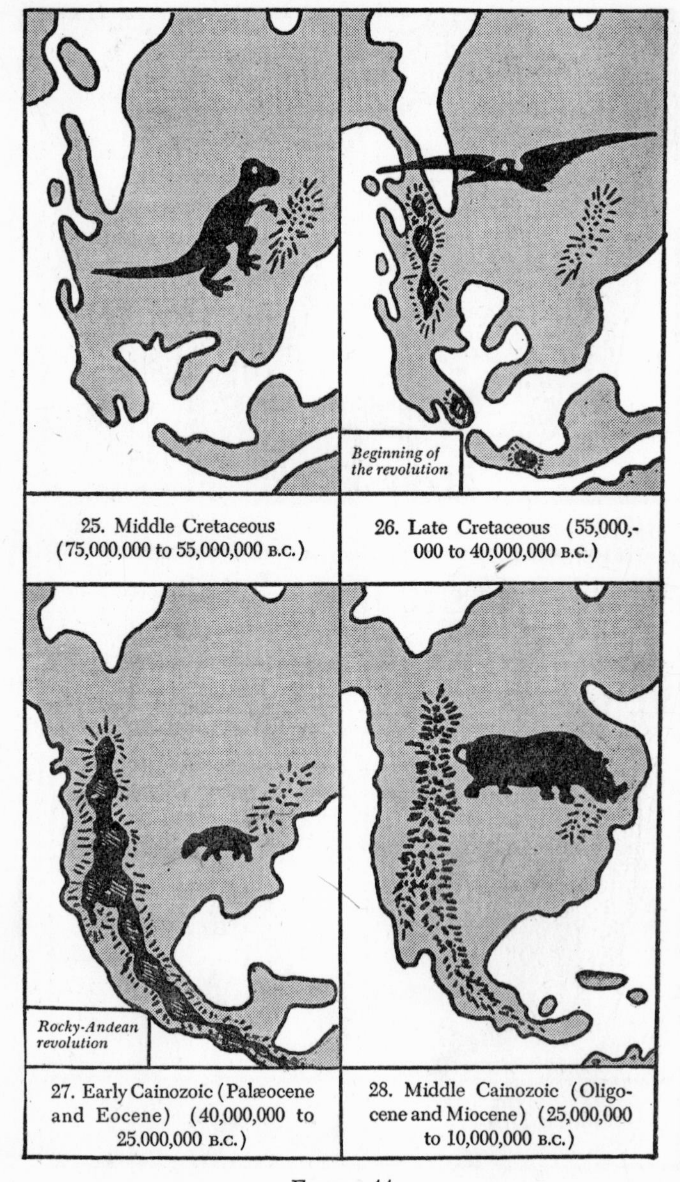
Beginning of
the revolution
25. Middle Cretaceous
(75,000,000 to 55,000,000 B.C.)
26. Late Cretaceous (55,000,-
000 to 40,000,000 B.C.)
Rocky-Andean
revolution
27. Early Cainozoic (Palæocene
and Eocene) (40,000,000 to
25,000,000 B.C.)
28. Middle Cainozoic (Oligocene and Miocene) (25,000,000
to 10,000,000 B.C.)

FIGURE 44

29. Late Cainozoic (Pliocene) (10,000,000 to 1,000,000 B.C.)

30. Latest Cainozoic (Pleistocene) (1,000,000 to 15,000 B.C.)

31. The Present

32. The Future

FIGURE 45

defined chapters. We have mentioned, however, that changes on a smaller scale were going on all the time, causing permanent alterations in the surface of our planet. In order to represent all these changes continuously, we should have to draw separate maps for each hundred years at least, and then run them through a motion-picture projector. Aside from the fact that present geologic knowledge is far from complete enough to make such an undertaking possible, a film in which each frame represents a century of the Earth's history would run continuously, day and night, for more than two weeks (at the standard film speed of 16 frames per second).

We are therefore reducing this project to a more modest scale, giving thirty-two separate maps representing the state of the continent of North America over a period of 500,000,000 years. These are adapted from the paleogeographic maps of Charles Schuchert, published in *Historical Geology* by Charles Schuchert and Carl O. Dunbar.

CHAPTER VIII

Climates of the Past

WE LIVE IN A GLACIAL EPOCH

AS WE have seen in Chapter VII, the entire history of the Earth is naturally divided into several long periods of submergence separated by comparatively short revolutionary epochs, when the continents were violently lifted up and newly formed mountains arose in many places on the surface of the Earth. The idea of high mountains is inseparably associated in our minds with a picture of shining ice caps and magnificent glaciers descending from the mountainous regions as broad slow rivers of ice (Plate XIVA). Even in subtropical regions the tops of high mountains permanently wear their white frosting, while closer to the poles all highlands are covered with thick sheets of eternal ice. In southern Chile and Alaska large glaciers descend from the coastal mountain ranges to the ocean, and the large pieces of ice breaking off from them are carried away by ocean currents, forming the giant floating icebergs.

An ice cap some 1,800,000 square kilometres in area and with a maximum thickness of more than 3 kilometres covers the island of Greenland,* while the isolated continent of Antarctica is covered by an eternal layer of ice

* The thickness of an ice layer is estimated by the ingenious method of echo sounding through ice. The sound waves produced by an explosion on the surface are reflected from the underlying rocks, and the delay in the arrival of this "bottom echo" gives us the ice thickness directly. This method is analogous to those used in the study of the crust by means of earthquake waves (Chapter V).

with a total area of 13,000,000 square kilometres and an estimated average thickness of about 1 kilometre.

Yet the present extent of the ice sheets, though covering large areas of the continental massifs, is considerably smaller than it used to be in the not so very distant past. The first indication that the present area of ice sheets is slowly decreasing is the well-known fact that most of the mountain glaciers of today are growing shorter and shorter every year.

But the most direct proof of much more extensive glaciation in the past can be found by studying the corresponding pages of the "Book of Sediments." Large areas of Northern Europe and North America are covered by very characteristic deposits known as "drift," consisting of "boulder clay" or "till" mixed with gravel and sand. For a long time the origin of this material presented an insoluble riddle to geologists, until in 1840, the Swiss scientist Louis Agassiz explained it as due to the work of moving sheets of ice. These large masses of ice, descending into the valleys from high mountainous regions, also leave deep scars on the surfaces of the exposed rocks and carry giant stones far away from their original sites.

To the surprise of contemporary geologists, Agassiz was able to prove not only that the flourishing valley of his native Switzerland, where he commenced his studies, were hidden under the glaciers descending from the Alpine heights not so long ago, but that another giant sheet of ice, coming from the Scandinavian highlands, covered much of Northern Europe. The distribution of glacial deposits left no doubt that at that time all of northern Germany, northern France, and the entire British Isles presented a landscape that can be seen today only by explorers travelling in Greenland or in Antarctica.

On this side of the Atlantic, several separate sheets of ice, descending from the Canadian highlands, covered about half the present area of the United States; not far from New York City one can find rocks polished by the moving ice sheets and giant stones carried by the glaciers for hundreds of miles only to be left in very unusual positions (Plate XIVB).

FIGURE 46
Cainozoic glaciation in the Northern and Southern Hemispheres. Large areas represent extensive continental glaciers; broken lines represent mountain glaciers. The glaciation of northern Siberia is uncertain.

Looking at the map of Figure 46, which shows the maximum extension of ice during that epoch, we notice that, although North America and Europe were hidden deep under the ice, the glaciation in Northern Asia was limited to a very few small areas. This striking fact is explainable by the absence of mountains in the north of Siberia and affords additional proof of the view that *glaciation is directly connected with the presence of high mountainous regions.*

It has been estimated that the total volume of ice piled upon the continents during the maximum stage of glaciation amounted to many million cubic kilometres, and that, since all this water must have been withdrawn from the ocean, *sea level at that time was about 100 metres lower than it is now*. This resulted, of course, in a much larger extension of the land, and at that time one could comfortably walk ten or twenty miles eastward from the present site of Atlantic City without even wetting one's feet.

Under the enormous weight of ice piled upon the northern parts of the continents the crust of the Earth was pressed down into the plastic mass underneath by as much as 200 metres in the region of the Great Lakes, and still more farther north. As soon as the ice vanished, these regions were inundated by the waters of the ocean, and the discovery of marine shells and even skeletons of whales at elevations of several hundred feet in Michigan and in upper New York State is indisputable proof that the present elevation of these regions is the result of the later isostatic adjustment of the crust.

We must also point out that careful study of glacial deposits, both in this country and in Europe, indicates that *there were at least four (and probably more) consecutive advances of ice, separated by long interglacial stages with relatively warmer climates*. In fact, during these interglacial stages the retreat of the ice sheets was even greater than it is at present,* so that we are forced to conclude that *we are still living in the closing stage of*

* It is interesting to note that the present area of glaciated regions is only three times as small as it was during the maximum phase of glaciation.

the last glacial period and that, before the next sheet of ice begins its advance upon our continents, the climate of North America, Europe and Asia is bound to become somewhat warmer than it is at present.

The time that has elapsed since the last extensive glaciation can be estimated rather exactly from study of the deposits left by the retreating ice sheet. The deposits that

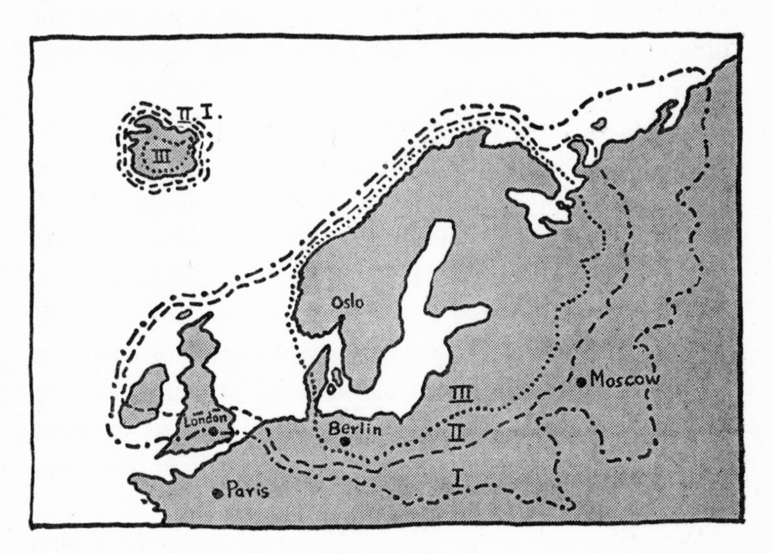

FIGURE 47
Maximum extension of the last three glacial sheets over Europe.

were formed in the glacial lakes bordering the southern edge of the retreating ice clearly show well-marked layers that correspond to summer and winter depositions. The material carried down by the streams originating in the melting ice during the summers consists of rough material known as "silt," usually light in colour. It is followed by the darker layers of fine clay formed during the winter months, when the lakes were frozen and the waters were much quieter. Studying these deposits in different localities ranging from the southern tip of Sweden to the lakes of central Norway, the Swedish geologist de Geer was able to prove that while the ice was retreating this distance, it formed about 13,500 deposition layers of silt and clay. This immediately gives us the number of years that have elapsed since Scandinavia first began to emerge from under the ice. Assuming the same rate of retreat for earlier epochs, we find that *the retreat of ice from Europe began about 25,000 years ago.*

Similar investigation carried out in the Western Hemisphere has led to the conclusion that the first retreat of ice from North America began at about the same time. In view of the fact that such a long period of time (from the human, not from the geological, viewpoint) was necessary to cover only one phase of a single glaciation period we must conclude that *the ice was advancing and retreating across the northern parts of the continents for several hundred thousand years during the most recent period of the Earth's history.*

Evidence of the analogous glaciation periods in the Southern Hemisphere is rather scarce, as the corresponding areas around the South Pole (40° to 70° south latitude) are mostly ocean wastes. It was found, however, that the snow line in the Andean highlands of Argentina, Chile, and Peru was once about one kilometre lower than it is at present, and there are indications of the existence of at least two cold waves with an intermediate warmer stage. The glaciers of New Zealand also used to be considerably larger, and there once were glaciers in Australia, which now has no ice at all.

IT USED TO BE WARMER

Leafing back through a couple of million pages of the "Book of Sediments," we find that the conditions of general glaciation are not at all typical of the history of the Earth, and that our planet used to have a considerably milder and more uniform climate during most of its existence. In fact, when we study the deposits of such a comparatively recent age as the Eocene period (which corresponds to the very beginning of the most recent revolution, about 40 million years ago), we find strong evidence that climatic zones were shifted northward at that time by as much as 20 or 30 degrees of latitude. In the Eocene deposits of continental Europe we find numerous fossils of palms and other plants, which indicate that that part of the world was then covered with rich subtropical vegetation. Palm groves must have been a common sight in southern England in those days. The same is true of North America: the fossilized leaves of magnolias, palms, and other subtropical plants have been found as far north as the states of Oregon and Washington.

While the areas now covered by temperate vegetation were occupied by tropical jungles, such ordinary trees as oak, chestnut, and maple were growing in Alaska, Greenland, Spitsbergen, and Northern Asia. Finally, the typical boreal plants, such as dwarf birch and dwarf willow, were very common in regions which are so far north that no vegetation at all can grow there today. Data concerning the Southern Hemisphere are again rather meagre, but the finding of coal deposits in several places along the shore of Antarctica indisputably proves that there were times when this continent, at present almost completely glaciated, was covered by rich vegetation.

Some idea of the differences between present climatic conditions and those existing before the beginning of

FIGURE 48
Distribution of vegetation zones in the Northern Hemisphere prior to the glacial periods, showing that subtropical forests extended as far north as London and Boston, whereas temperate vegetation could be found in southern Greenland, Iceland, and Spitsbergen.

general glaciation can be gained from the map of Figure 48.

In addition to the data of palæobotany, we also have similar data from palæozoology. Thus, for example, marine molluscs of the type now found only in warm seas existed as far north as the shores of Alaska, while rhinoceroses and tigers ranged across the present area of the United States! Going back still further in time, we find that the conditions of milder and more uniform climate were typical of the whole period of Mesozoic submergence and that traces of extensive glaciation are first noticed only in connexion with the Appalachian revolution, that is, about 150,000,000 years ago.

The most conclusive evidence about this ancient glaciation was found in South America, South Africa, India, and Australia, and the thickness of the glacial deposits shows that it was longer and more intense than the recent glaciation of Europe and North America. There are also definite indications that there were several distinct cold waves separated by warmer interglacial periods; the deposits found in many localities of Eastern Australia, Tasmania, and New Zealand bear the records of at least three such successive advances of ice.

In the Northern Hemisphere, the Appalachian revolution was also followed by the advance of ice, but the existing records show that the glaciation was comparatively mild and limited to a small area. This must have been due either to the absence of extensive highlands (as in the case of Siberia during the recent glacial epoch) or to the arid climate, which did not provide enough moisture for the formation of extensive continental glaciers.

Going still further back in time, we again encounter a warm climate during the entire period of Late Palæozoic submergence, and then again an extensive glaciation during the Caledonian revolution (300,000,000 B.C.), which left numerous deposits in Alaska, Norway, and

South Africa. Still earlier glacial deposits have been found to correspond to the Pre-Cambrian revolution that opens the historic period of the Earth's life.

Although the reading of the "Book of Sediments" becomes more and more difficult as we go back to more distant epochs, *there seems to be no doubt that extensive glaciation periods were always connected with the revolutionary epochs of general continental upheaval and mountain folding, and that each of these glaciations consisted of a number of successive cold waves, which caused the ice sheets to move back and forth across the continental surfaces.*

DO THE POLES WANDER ACROSS THE EARTH'S SURFACE?

The unusual climatic changes recorded in the "Book of Sediments"—the existence of subtropical forests in Central Europe and the subsequent appearance of thick layers of ice, the glaciation of the subtropical regions of India, and other related facts—caused many geologists and geophysicists to assume that important changes in the situation of continents and the position of the poles must have been taking place during the past epochs of the Earth's history. Basing their considerations on the original hypothesis of "continental drift" (see Chapters III and VII), with the additional assumption that the solid crust of the Earth can slide as a whole over the plastic material forming the interior of our planet, Wegener and a number of other scientists tried to reconstruct the relative positions of continents and poles to fit the climatic data supplied by historical geology. Thus, in order to explain the glaciation that took place simultaneously in South

America, South Africa, Australia, and India during the Appalachian revolution, they assumed that these lands were then much closer together than they are at present, and that the South Pole was situated roughly in the centre of the group. The corresponding site of the North Pole would be somewhere in the North Pacific, not far from the Hawaiian Islands. It was also assumed by various authors that the North Pole shifted to Alaska around the beginning of the Cainozoic era (in the Eocene period) and still later to the southern part of Greenland, thus causing extensive glaciation in North America and Europe. The warmer climate of recent times was considered to be the result of the subsequent displacement of the pole from Greenland to its present position. In Figure 49 we give one of these endeavours (due to Kreichgauer) to explain the climatic changes observed during the various epochs of the Earth's history by the migration of the poles.*

Although this picture of "drifting continents" and "wandering poles" presents inexhaustible food for our imagination and can be fitted into almost any given distribution of climate, owing to a large degree of freedom in choosing the position of the various elements involved, it can hardly stand up under criticism based upon our present knowledge of the properties of the globe. In fact, as we have already seen in Chapter VII, the basaltic bottom of the oceans is much too rigid to permit of any changes in the relative position of the continents; if such displacements actually occurred, they must have occurred at the very beginning of the Earth's history, when the basalt surface was still in a liquid state.

* The reader will, of course, understand that when we speak of the "migration" of the poles across the Earth's surface, we actually mean the sliding of the Earth's solid crust relative to its plastic interior.

The sliding of the crust as a whole over the plastic interior layers is possible even now, of course, but Harold Jeffreys showed that, taking into account the high vis-

FIGURE 49
Hypothetical migration of the North Pole according to Kreichgauer. This hypothesis, however, cannot be reconciled with our present knowledge of the properties of the Earth and the distribution of vegetation in the past.

cosity of the plastic masses, we can hardly expect the poles to have changed their position by more than a few degrees during the entire course of geological time. Besides, it is very difficult to conceive of forces that could have moved the poles along a line such as that shown, for example, in Figure 49.

More recent data of palæobotany and palæozoology seem to afford direct refutation of the pole movements assumed by Wegener and others. Thus, for example, placing the North Pole in Alaska during the early Cainozoic era (Figure 49) in order to account for the subtropical vegetation of Europe would condemn Alaska itself and all the surrounding areas to a very severe boreal climate, whereas it is known that these regions were covered by temperate and even partly subtropical vegetation at the very time (compare the map of Figure 48).

It is therefore necessary to assume that the relative position of continents and poles was very much the same during all of geologic history as it is at present.

WHAT CAUSED PERIODIC "COLD WAVES"?

In order to understand the causes of the glaciations that occur periodically on the surface of our globe, we have to remember that we are dealing here with a double periodicity. First of all, *extensive glaciations take place only during the periods of the Earth's history that follow the great revolutions, when the surface of the continents is elevated and covered with high mountains.* This periodicity simply indicates that the existence of such elevations is a prerequisite for the formation of thick sheets of ice, which, growing larger and larger, descend from the mountains and cover extensive areas of the surrounding plains.

But *within each glacial era corresponding to a given revolution there are also periodic changes considerably shorter in duration;* while the mountains are still standing, the ice advances and retreats across the plains many times in succession. This second periodicity is evidently independent of changes in the structural characteristics of the Earth's surface, and must be ascribed to real changes in temperature. Since the heat balance on the surface of the Earth is wholly regulated by the amount of solar radiation falling on it, we must look for possible factors that can affect the amount of incident solar radiation. Factors of this sort may be: (1) variations of the transparency of the terrestrial atmosphere; (2) periodic changes in solar activity; and (3) changes in the Earth's rotation around the Sun.

The purely atmospheric explanation of the variability of climate, which is still favoured by many climatologists, rests on the hypothesis that, for one reason or another, the amount of carbon dioxide in our atmosphere is subject to periodic fluctuations with time. Since this constituent of the air is largely responsible for the absorption of heat radiation, a relatively slight decrease in the carbon-dioxide content of the atmosphere might have caused a considerable drop in the surface temperature, resulting in the excessive ice formation characteristic of glacial periods. It must be borne in mind, however, that although such an explanation is in itself quite possible, the reason for these supposed periodic fluctuations in the composition of the air is not at all clear. Moreover, there is no way of checking whether the extensive glaciations of the past were actually connected with a variation in the air's carbon-dioxide content.

The hypothesis that seeks to explain the cold spells by variability of solar activity suffers from the same sort of indefiniteness. To be sure, we do observe periodic changes in solar radiation, caused by the varying number of sunspots, which reaches a maximum every 10 or 12 years. It is also true that during the years of sunspot maxima the average terrestial temperature drops about one degree centigrade because of the decrease in the amount of radiation received. But there are no indications, either observational or theoretical, of variations of solar activity persisting for thousands of years. Here, as with the carbon-dioxide hypothesis, it appears to be quite impossible to check the coincidence of past glacial ages with minima of solar activity.

The last of these three hypotheses is not subject to these strictures, however, and, as we shall see, it not only enables us to understand the causes of periodic glaciation, but also makes it possible to fix their dates in excellent agreement with geologic evidence.

The reader will remember that the seasonal changes on the surface of the Earth are due to the fact that its axis of rotation is inclined to the plane of its orbit, so that for six months the Northern Hemisphere (and another six months the Southern Hemisphere) is turned toward the Sun (Figure 50). Owing to the longer duration of the day and the more vertical incidence of the solar rays, the hemisphere turned toward the Sun receives considerably more heat and has a summer season, whereas the opposite hemisphere goes through the period of winter cold.

It must be remembered, however, that the Earth's orbit is not exactly a circle, but an ellipse, so that the Earth gets closer to the Sun at some points of its trajectory than at others. At the present time the earth passes through the perihelion of its orbit (i.e., through the point closest to the Sun) at the end of December, and reaches its maximum distance from the Sun at the end of June. *Consequently, winters in the Northern Hemisphere must be somewhat milder than in the Southern, whereas northern summers must be somewhat cooler.* We know from astronomical observation that the distance to the Sun in December is some 3 per cent less than in June, so that the difference in the

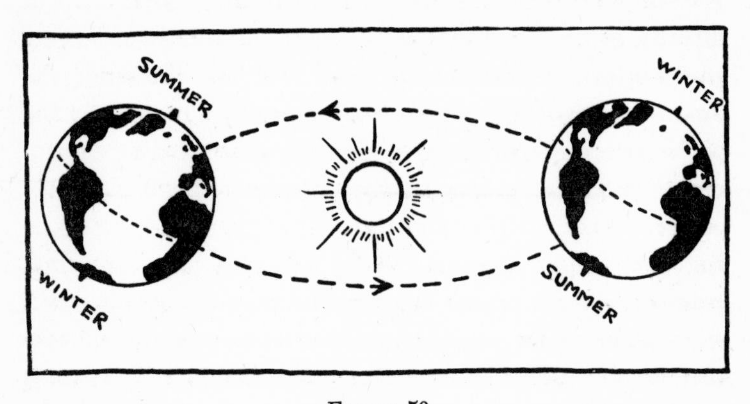

FIGURE 50
Familiar explanation of the seasonal changes in the Northern and Southern Hemispheres.

heat received in opposite hemispheres should amount to 6 per cent, since the intensity of radiation decreases as the inverse square of the distance. Using the relationship between the amount of radiation received and the temperature of the surface,* we find that *at the present time the mean temperature of northern summers must be 4 to 5° C. (7 to 9° F.) lower, and the mean temperatures of northern winters 4 to 5 degrees higher, than the corresponding values for the Southern Hemisphere.*

* If L_1 and L_2 represent the amount of heat received, and T_1 and T_2 represent the corresponding surface temperatures, we obtain the equation:

$$\frac{T_1 + 273^\circ\text{C.}}{T_2 + 273^\circ\text{C.}} = \sqrt[4]{\frac{L_1}{L_2}}$$

One might think that these differences between the two hemispheres cannot contribute to the explanation of glacial periods, since the colder summers will be compensated for by warmer winters, and vice versa. This is not true, however, because the relative effect of temperature variations upon the formation of ice is quite different for summers and winters. In fact, if the temperature is already below the freezing point (as it usually is during the winter), its further decrease will not influence the amount of snowfall, since all the humidity present in the air is precipitated anyhow. On the other hand, the increase of radiation during the summer will considerably accelerate the melting and removal of the ice formed during the winter months. Thus we must conclude that *colder summers favour the formation of ice sheets much more than colder winters, and that consequently the conditions necessary for extensive glaciation are at present realized in the Northern Hemisphere.*

"But," the reader will probably ask, "why don't we then have glaciation in Europe and North America at the present time, if the climatic conditions favour it?" The answer to this question lies in the absolute value of the temperature difference; and it seems that the cooling of 4 to 5° C. (7 to 9° F.) is just below the amount necessary to cause the growth of ice sheets. As we have seen above, the glaciers of the Northern Hemisphere are at present retreating rather than advancing. But the balance between the amount of snowfall during the winters and the amount of melted ice during the summers is a very delicate one, and *a drop in summer temperature that is only two or three times larger may completely reverse the situation.*

Looking for the causes of larger temperature differences,

which might have caused extensive glaciations of the past, we must turn our attention to possible changes in the direction of the Earth's axis of rotation and in its orbital motion around the Sun. It is well known that the rotation axis of the Earth is slowly changing its position in space, describing a cone whose central line is perpendicular to the plane of the orbit; a phenomenon analogous to that observed in an ordinary spinning top (Figure 51a). This motion of the Earth's axis is known as *precession;** it was explained by Newton as due to the attractive forces of the Sun and the Moon on the equatorial bulge of the rotating globe. This motion of the Earth's axis in space is very slow, taking about 26,000 years to complete the entire cycle. It is clear that the phenomenon of precession will periodically change the situation described on the previous pages, and *that approximately every 13,000 years the Earth will pass through its perihelion with its Northern and Southern Hemispheres alternately turned toward the Sun.* It is also clear that this phenomenon, alternating the climatic differences between the two hemispheres, cannot bring about a more intensive decrease of temperature in either of them; if at present "we could, but do not actually, have an ice age at New York" the same formula will be applicable to Buenos Aires 13,000 years hence.

In addition to ordinary precession, there are other perturbations of the motion of the Earth caused by the action of other planets, by Jupiter, in particular, which, proud of its great mass, tackles almost every little planet of the solar system. The study of these perturbations represents

* The name "precession" was introduced in 125 B.C. by Hipparchus, who noticed that the "point of equinox" (i.e., the point on the celestial sphere where the ecliptic crosses the equator) is slowly "preceding" or "stepping forward" to meet the Sun.

the chief subject of the science of celestial mechanics, which has been brought to the highest degree of precision by the work of many great mathematicians of the past and the present.

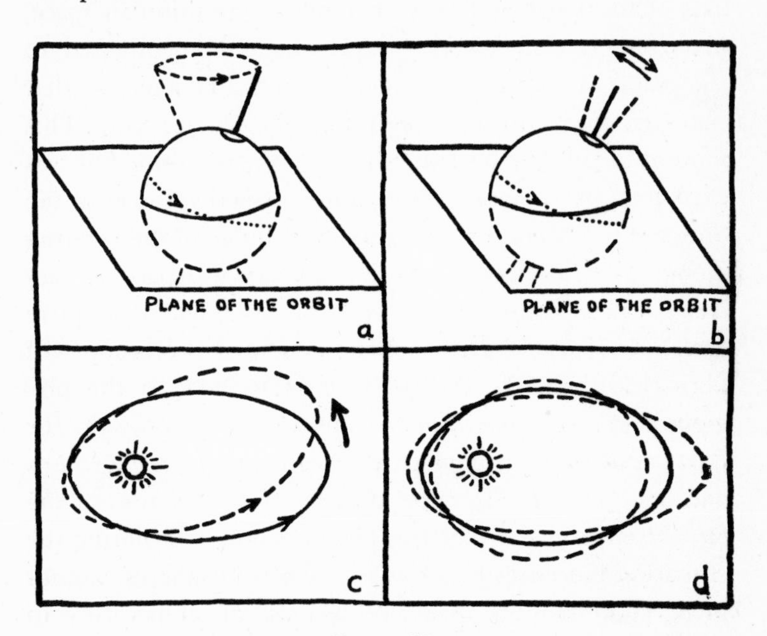

FIGURE 51
Variations of the elements of the Earth's motion.
a. Precession of the axis of rotation.
b. Variation of inclination to the plane of the orbit.
c. Precession of the Earth's orbit.
d. Changes in the eccentricity of the orbit.
(All variations are greatly exaggerated in the diagram.)

We learn from celestial mechanics that the inclination of the Earth's axis of rotation to the plane of its orbit (which is unaffected by ordinary precession) is subject to periodic changes with a period of about 40,000 years (Figure 51b). Since the very existence of the summer and winter seasons is due to this inclination (compare Figure 50), we must conclude that *larger inclinations increase the differences between the two hemispheres and lead to warmer summers and colder winters.* On the other hand, the straightening of the Earth's axis leads to a more uniform climate; the differences between seasons would disappear completely if the axis were perpendicular to the plane of the orbit.

Nor does the orbit of the Earth itself remain unchanged; it rotates slowly around the Sun, with periodic increases and decreases in its eccentricity (Figure 51c, d). Although both changes show a roughly periodic character, the periods vary from 60,000 to 120,000 years, and in order to get an exact picture of these variations one is obliged to use the complicated calculations of celestial mechanics. Fortunately enough, the methods of celestial mechanics are so fabulously precise that *the entire picture of the behaviour of the Earth's orbit can be reconstructed as far back as one million years with a probable error of not more than 10 per cent.*

The rotation of the orbit around the Sun obviously produces the same effect as the precession of the Earth's axis, and the two phenomena must simply be added together.

Periodic changes of eccentricity are of great importance for climatic conditions in both hemispheres. *During epochs of large elongation of the orbit, the Earth is especially far from the Sun while passing through the most distant point of its trajectory, and the amount of heat received by both hemispheres at that time is exceptionally low.* According to exact calculations, the eccentricity of the Earth's orbit 180,000 years ago, for instance, was 2½ times larger than it is at present, from which it follows that the temperature difference between the Northern and Southern Hemispheres must have been about 9° to 10° C. (16° to 18° F.) (see footnote, page 180).

Although the temperature changes resulting from any one of the above causes may not be very important, we must remember that if they had all been acting in the same direction at a certain epoch of the Earth's history, the combined effect might have been rather large. Thus, during the epoch when the eccentricity of the orbit was especially large, the inclination of the axis especially small, and the summer season in the Northern Hemisphere occurred while the Earth was passing through the most distant part of its elongated orbit, the amount of heat received in this hemisphere during the summer months must have been exceptionally low.

On the other hand, a smaller eccentricity of the orbit combined with the opposite inclination of the axis of rotation must have caused considerably milder climatic conditions in this hemisphere.

Using the data on the elements of the Earth's motion obtained by the methods of celestial mechanics, a Yugoslav geophysicist, A. Milankovitch, constructed a chart representing climatic variations in the Northern and Southern Hemispheres due to these purely astronomical causes. One of his curves, for the Northern Hemisphere, representing the amount of solar heat received at 65° north latitude during 650,000 past summers, is reproduced in Figure 52. This curve shows that the unidirectional action of all the three causes mentioned above must have taken place in the years 25,000 B.C., 70,000 B.C., 115,000 B.C., 190,000 B.C., 230,000 B.C., 425,000 B.C., 475,000 B.C., 550,000 B.C., and 590,000 B.C. Comparing this theoretical curve with the empirical curve obtained by geologists, which represents the maximum extension of the glaciers of the past (as determined by glacial deposits), we find that the agreement is even better than could have been expected. This proves beyond any doubt the correctness of the above explanation of glacial periods. Similar results

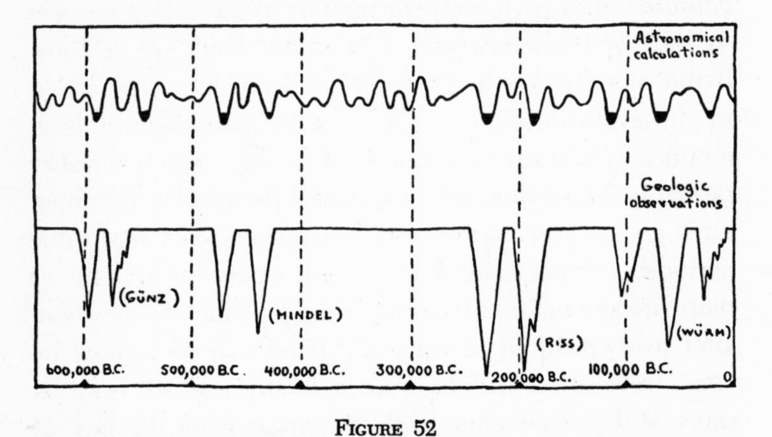

FIGURE 52

The upper graph represents the variations of temperature during summers at 65° north latitude (after Milankovitch). The lower graph gives the different glaciation periods as deduced from geological data. The names in parentheses are those of the river valleys in which the deposits formed by various advances of ice were discovered and studied.

were also obtained for the Southern Hemisphere, but in that hemisphere the comparison of theory and observation is much less decisive because of our comparatively meagre knowledge concerning glacial advances there.

It is apparent that there must have been a number of separate glacial advances; the geological division of the glacial epochs into only four or five periods is due to the fact that these separate advances have been always associated in close groups of two or three.

In concluding this chapter, we must remind the reader

once more that *the periodic succession of warmer and colder climates, caused by purely astronomical factors, must have been taking place at intervals of less than a 100,000 years throughout the entire geological history of our planet. It was only during the mountainous stages of the Earth's evolution, however, that conditions were favourable enough for the formation of extensive glaciers by each of these successive cold waves.* Since we are now living more or less in the midst of a revolutionary epoch in the evolution of our planet, with a number of high mountains already standing and a still larger number probably impending, we must expect the ice that retreated some 30,000 years ago to come back again, and that these periodic advances and retreats will continue as long as there are any mountains in northern latitudes. Only when, after many millions of years, all the elevations formed by "our" revolution will have been finally washed away by rains, will glaciers completely disappear from the face of the Earth, the climate become milder and more uniform, and the changes in the Earth's orbit and the inclination of its axis result only in relatively unimportant variations of the average yearly temperatures in different localities. And then, after another hundred or two hundred million years, a new revolution and new periodic glaciations will ensue.

CHAPTER IX

Life on the Earth

THE ORIGIN OF LIFE

IF WE remember that about five billion years ago our planet was a red-hot sphere of molten matter, we must inevitably conclude that all the forms of life that now flourish on its surface must have come into being only after this surface was covered with a solid crust and had cooled down sufficiently to permit the existence of complex organic substances. More specifically, we can associate the appearance of living beings with the epoch when torrents of warm water fell from the sky on the slowly cooling surface of the earth, forming extensive ocean basins, which have always been recognized as the cradle of primeval life.

Since, according to the evidence of palæontology, life could not have been present on the Earth during the early stages of its existence, but came into being almost as soon as the conditions became favourable, the great question confronts us: "How and why did life appear on our planet?" Not so long ago, one of the favourite explanations of the appearance of life on our planet was the hypothesis first advanced by Richter in 1865, according to which life itself is eternal and is carried from one planetary system to another in the form of minute living spores or "cosmozoans." Whenever such a "cosmozoan" reaches a planet on which the conditions are favourable for its development, it begins to multiply and, through the long progress of organic evolution, leads to all the higher forms of life. Svante Arrhenius pointed out that these world-travelling life-carriers could attain considerable velocities in their journey through space, driven forward as they were by the radiation pressure of light emitted by the stars. He calculated, in fact, that a small plant spore, carried to the upper limit of the atmosphere by some ascending air current and then "blown away" by the radiation of the Sun, can attain a velocity of about 100 kilometres per second. Travelling with such velocity, the spore would require but a few months to reach the other planets of our system, and in 10,000 years it would cover the distance separating us from the nearest star. It must be borne in mind, however, that the ultraviolet rays of our Sun, which are almost entirely absorbed by the terrestrial atmosphere, will rapidly kill any micro-organism that ventures beyond this protective shield. Thus, life must be inevitably extinguished in such travelling spores long before they are able to reach even the nearest planet. Besides, quite apart from the problem of the preservation of life during the long interstellar voyage, the "cosmozoan hypothesis" becomes rather senseless in the light of modern knowledge.

This "physical creation of the universe" must have taken place during the epoch immediately preceding the formation of our Earth and other planetary systems, and, since it is obvious that *at that time no life could exist anywhere in the universe,* the problem of the origin of life has to be faced anew. Nor is there much sense in the efforts to push the important question of the creation of life into the distant corners of space that are in no respect different from our own good Earth.

But if life really originated on our planet as the result of some complicated rearrangement of previously dead matter, we must inquire into the nature of the processes that led to the formation of primitive living organisms and the conditions necessary for this important transformation.

The problem of the origin of life understandably counts as one of the most exciting questions in the natural sciences, but in spite of almost endless speculation on this subject, it is still far from its final solution. Of course, the transition between dead and living matter must have been very gradual, and over very long periods of time it must have been impossible to tell whether a given lump of matter belonged to the animate or the innanimate world. It is probably safe to assume that the appearance of "real" living things was preceded by the formation of various complex organic compounds of carbon, which were later used as "moulding clay" for the building of primitive organisms.

The study of living organisms leads to the conclusion that the most important substances participating in their structure are the complex organic compounds known as *proteins.* The molecular weight of protein molecules ranges from tens of thousands to many millions, thus dwarfing even the largest molecules ordinarily encountered in inorganic or organic chemistry. However, closer inspection reveals that this apparent complexity of protein molecules can be reduced to comparatively simple laws of structural regularity. When proteins are heated in water solution they break up into relatively simple molecules known as *amino acids.* It has been shown that there are altogether twenty different amino acids which enter into the structure of proteins, and that, in fact, protein molecules are nothing except long chains of amino acids aligned like beads on a string. Thus, in order to understand the origin of proteins, we must first understand the origin of the amino acids from which they are formed. An important step in this direction was made by the American chemist Harold Urey who showed that various amino acids could have been formed in the primordial atmosphere of the Earth under the action of ultraviolet radiation coming from the Sun. In fact, the atmosphere of our globe during the early days of its existence seems to have been quite different from what it is now. Whereas the atmosphere of today contains large amounts of oxygen, the primordial gaseous envelope of the Earth was mostly composed of hydrogen and its simple compounds, such as methane (H_4C), ammonia (H_3N), and water vapour (H_2O). As was proved by direct experiment, the mixture of these gases subjected to a prolonged irradiation by ultraviolet light gives rise to more complex molecules of the amino acids, the basic components of all proteins. After being formed at the upper layers of the primordial terrestrial atmosphere where the ultraviolet radiation of the sun is most intensive, the molecules of various amino acids slowly drifted down, becoming dissolved in the waters of the oceans which themselves had only recently been formed.

The next large step which we must make here is the transition from the water solution of amino acids, which any good chemist can easily prepare in his laboratory, to the long amino-acid chains representing various protein molecules. This must have resulted from a natural tendency of amino-acid molecules to stick together, thus forming sequences hundreds and thousands of units long. This process, known as polymerization, is admittedly extremely slow, but the first preparatory steps for the origin of life had billions of years in which to be accomplished. Thus, we can visualize a long sequence of chemical reactions slowly taking place in the primordial ocean and leading gradually to the formation of more and more complex protein molecules suitable for building the living organisms.

But the "spark of life" is given not only by the chemical constitution but also by the definite *organization* of material. In order to understand the transition from lifeless organic matter to living organisms, we must pay special attention to the processes which could have differentiated the primary dead material and organized it into separate living units. Some light was thrown on this most obscure stage of the organic evolution by the work of the Russian biologist Oparin.

One of the most important points to be taken into account in any discussion of the nature of life is the fact that living protoplasm, out of which all animals and plants are constructed, is a so-called *colloidal solution* of various complex organic substances in water. Colloidal solutions of inorganic or organic matter actually represent a very fine emulsion, consisting of minute electrically charged particles of the substance in question, suspended in water and held apart by the repulsive electrical forces between the charges. Since pure water is a very poor conductor of electricity, the particles retain their charges for an indefinitely long time, and the emulsion does not settle down. If, however, we take a colloidal solution of, let us say, gold and add some salt to it, thus increasing the water's electrical conductivity, the separate particles will rapidly lose their charges and begin to fuse together. This will lead to the formation of larger and larger particles (coagulation), which will soon precipitate a thin layer of gold on the bottom of the vessel. We can also cause such precipitation by mixing together two different colloids, the particles of which carry electrical charges of opposite sign. In this case, the repulsion between similar particles will be compensated for by the attraction between particles with opposite charges, and coagulation will immediately follow.

Colloidal solutions of organic substances, such as ordinary gum arabic, differ from all other solutions of this type in that the molecules of carbon compounds possess a strong chemical affinity for water. The colloidal particles of these substances are always surrounded by concentric layers of water molecules, as indicated in Figure 53b. The molecules of water forming the first layer are firmly attached to the surface of the particle, whereas the successive outer layers are bound more and more loosely. As a result, each particle is surrounded by a stable "water mem-

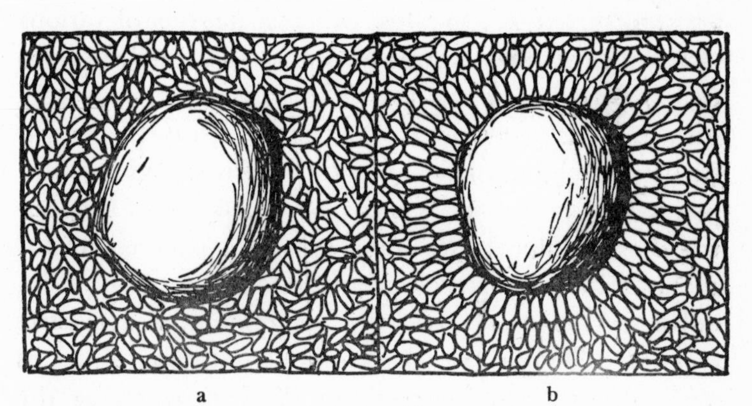

FIGURE 53
a. Inorganic colloidal particle. Water molecules move freely around the particle.
b. Organic colloidal particle. Water molecules stick to the surface, forming concentric layers.

brane," although there is no real demarcation between the water molecules of the membrane and the water molecules of the solution.

The existence of such a water membrane surrounding the colloidal particles of complex carbon compounds adds greatly to the stability of these systems and probably represents the most important factor in the structure of living matter. The water membrane prevents the particles from losing their electrical charge, and even if a salt is added to the solution, coagulation will not take place. If we mix together two organic colloidal solutions possessing opposite charges, the particles begin to attract one another, but they will be unable to fuse together because of the water membranes covering them. Instead of a solid precipitate, in this case we obtain a semi-liquid jelly-like substance usually known as *coazervate.* For example, mixing together (under suitable conditions) the colloidal solutions of gelatine and gum arabic (both of which, in their

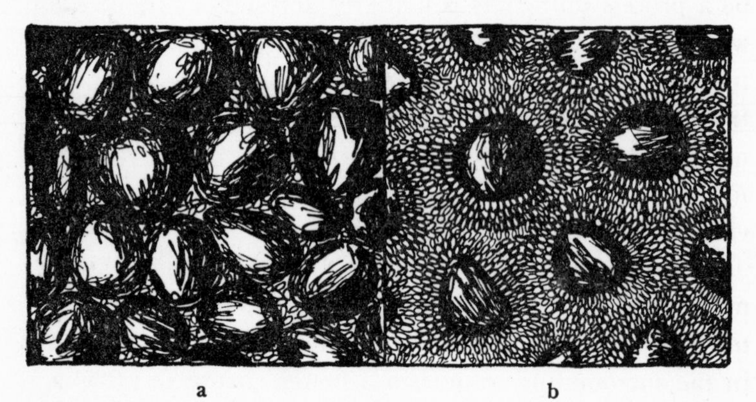

FIGURE 54

a. Coagulation of an inorganic colloid. Particles come together, forming a solid substance.

b. Coazervation of an organic colloid. Particles are separated by a water membrane, forming a jelly.

dilute states, are clear, homogeneous liquids) we will observe the formation of minute droplets of complex gelatine–gum-arabic coazervate, which separates from the rest of the liquid and makes the mixture look opaque.

Careful studies by numerous investigators show that the properties of coazervate droplets present many interesting analogies with the properties of living protoplasm. In particular, these droplets possess the ability of absorbing various substances dissolved in the surrounding solution, thus increasing their size and weight. According to Oparin, *the formation of coazervates from the various organic substances dissolved in the water of the primeval ocean represented the most important step toward the development of life on our planet,* and one may regard these minute droplets, formed by ordinary physicochemical processes but already possessing the ability to grow, as the "missing link" between the inorganic and organic worlds. Beginning with this stage the evolution of organic matter ceased to be a process uniformly distributed throughout the ocean waters, and each separate coazervate droplet was bound to live a life of its own. The individuality of life resulting from the separation of such droplets from the previously more or less continuous solution must have led at once to the "struggle for life" and Darwin's process of the "survival of the fittest."

Those coazervate droplets whose chemical constitution made them better adapted to existing conditions and better able to assimilate various chemical substances dissolved in the surrounding water had a better chance to grow at the expense of the material taken away from the other, "weaker" droplets. Although this competitive process bore in itself the fundamental features of life, it still had a rather elementary character and could easily be mistaken for purely inorganic processes, such as the growing of larger droplets of fog at the expense of smaller ones. But as time went on, the process of "natural selection" of those coazervate droplets that had developed a better method of food assimilation steadily increased the gap between these newly formed organisms and ordinary inorganic material. The fittest, and therefore the most rapidly growing, droplet organisms could not, however, go on growing indefinitely, because the ratio of their surface to their total volume was becoming smaller and smaller.* Since all primitive organisms assimilated their food through their surfaces, the increase of "flesh" to be fed through a given area of "skin" was turning against those that had attained an especially large size. This must have led to the splitting of very large individuals into two equal parts, a process that, in a very much advanced form, can be now observed as complex *cell division.* The daughter organisms produced by splitting now had the advantage of a larger active surface together with the hereditary good constitution, and carried on the banners of the race.

IS THE "LIFE-CREATING" PROCESS CONTINUING AT PRESENT?

Before proceeding with the discussion of organic evolution, we may ask ourselves *whether the process of "life creation" described above took place only once in the dim past of the Earth's history, or whether it can be assumed to be continuing at the present time?* Of course, nobody believes now, as was customary a century ago, that flies orig-

* With the increase of linear dimensions the surface increases as the square of the radius, and the volume as the cube of the radius.

inate spontaneously from decaying meat, mice from mud and dirt, and mould from moisture on the walls. Moreover the famous experiments of Pasteur and his school definitely proved that even the simplest micro-organisms cannot appear spontaneously in hermetically sealed vessels, the contents of which were carefully boiled beforehand in order to kill all existing germs. But the process of "life creation" described above is extremely slow, and after all nobody can be sure of what would happen if a bottle of pasteurized milk should be opened a couple of millions of years after it was sealed! On the other hand, since the conditions necessary for the origin of life must have been about the same as the conditions necessary for its further development, it is difficult to find any *a priori* reason why the slow transformation of inorganic matter into primitive living organisms cannot be continuing even today.

It can be argued, of course, that the total amount of organic substances originally dissolved in the primeval oceans is now largely reduced, having been used up in the building of existing plants and animals. But there is also no doubt that the ocean waters of today still contain large amounts of organic matter (originating to a large extent in the decay of living organisms), and it is difficult to see why this matter cannot be used in building up new life.

One may also say that, even if new life is being created at the present time, the primitive organisms formed in such a process must be immediately eaten up by higher animal species and would have no chance of developing a new line of their own. However, if such a point of view were generally correct, the oceans of today would be entirely devoid of any simple forms of life, since all the smaller organisms would be eaten up by fish. Reducing this argument to absurdity, we should also expect that there would be no grass on the Earth, since it would be all eaten up by cows; and no cows, since they would be eaten up by man. . . .

It seems that the strongest argument in favour of the theory extending the genealogical tree of any living being all the way back to the first appearance of life on our planet lies in the fundamental similarity between all living things. It can be argued, for instance, that such a complex substance as chlorophyll,* which is present in all plants, could not have originated independently in several unrelated lines of evolution, and that consequently all the members of the plant kingdom must be direct descendants of a certain "first plant."

It must be borne in mind, however, that since we still know very little about the laws of evolution, *we can never be sure as to how much of the observed similarity between living things stems from direct heredity and how much is due to the general frame of development that nature imposes on all living organisms.* In Chapter IV we saw, for example, that astronomical observations of the planet Mars strongly suggest that its surface is covered by some kind of vegetation, which is green in colour during the spring months and brown during the autumns and winters. The green colour of Martian vegetation definitely indicates that the leaves of the plants growing on Mars contain chlorophyll, probably identical with that of the terrestrial flora. Following the above argument, one would be in-

* Chlorophyll is a complex organic substance which gives plants their green colouring and serves to extract their food from the air by decomposing atmospheric carbon dioxide and using the carbon to build up complex organic substances.

clined to believe that the Martian plants originated from some seeds carried over from the Earth (or vice versa), whereas we have already seen that such a transfer of life, even between neighbouring planets, must be regarded as quite impossible. It seems much more reasonable to believe that the Martian vegetation developed quite independently, and has green colour simply because the best chemical substance for the assimilation of the carbon dioxide of the air is green chlorophyll. In the very same way the similarity of the snowflake figures on the Earth and on some distant planet should be ascribed to the general properties of water crystals, and not to an "interplanetary snowstorm."

Thus there seems to be no definite ground for believing that all living things existing at present on the Earth are the direct descendants of some "bacterial Adam" living sometime between 1,000,000,000 and 2,000,000,000 B.C. Nor is it wholly impossible that the great-great-great-great . . . great-grandparents of certain simple plants and animals now in existence may have been a couple of ordinary, unpretentious molecules as recently as the Mesozoic or even the Cainozoic era. On the other hand, there is also no doubt that most of the higher organisms must have passed through a very long sequence of intermediate forms, and that their genealogy extends to a much more distant past.

All the foregoing arguments for and against the point of view that the original "life-creating" process is still going on at present are all on the theoretical side. We may ask, however, whether any direct evidence can be obtained from observation of the living world, and whether there is any chance of finding the "missing link" between living and dead matter. The answer to this question is very difficult, of course, since, even if the representatives of such transitional stages of evolution are being continuously formed in ocean water today, they will easily escape detection because of their extremely small size and their comparatively small number.* It may be mentioned, however, that the study of ooze obtained from great depths of the ocean indicates the presence of some organic matter in the form of jelly sediments, and it is not entirely impossible that in this case we have before our eyes the state of organic matter "preparing to become alive." Some investigators are also of the opinion that the recently discovered "subbacteria" or "viruses," which are so small as to preclude microscopic study of their structure, may represent the most primitive organisms occupying the intermediate stage between animate and inanimate matter.

THE FIRST STEPS OF ORGANIC EVOLUTION

Since the earliest forms of life were limited to miniature soft-bodied organisms, there is not much chance of finding any extensive evidence of these first living beings among the early fragmented pages of the "Book of Sediments." There is, however, an abundance of indirect evidence. As we have said, the thick layers of marble found in various places on the Earth represent strongly metamorphized deposits of ordinary limestone, formed probably more than a billion years ago. It is well established at present that the more recent deposits of limestone are due largely to the work of simple micro-organisms, so that we may conclude with some degree of certainty that such simple forms

* The comparative rarity of these early products of organic evolution should be expected for the very same reason as the rarity of newborn babies, compared with the rest of the population.

of organic life were already in existence in that distant past.

The deposits formed during these early epochs of the Earth's history also contain a certain amount of carbon in the form of thin graphite layers. Although the presence of carbon can also be attributed to volcanic activity, its distribution through the rocks makes it more likely that it originated as the result of the decay of organic matter and was metamorphized into graphite when the deposits were pushed deeper into the Earth and became subject to very high pressures and temperatures. All this indicates that life was present in its very elementary forms more than a billion years ago, and that the absence of "true" fossils, such as we find in the later deposits, is simply due to the fact that at this early stage of development living organisms did not yet have rigid skeletons which could have made lasting impressions on the folded pages of the book of the Earth's history.

If through some miraculous device we were able to move back in time and transport ourselves to the year 1,000,000,000 B.C., the tepid waters of newly formed oceans and the rocky slopes of the primeval continental massifs would afford us a rather lifeless view. Only through careful study would we be able to find that life is already present on the surface of the planet, and that numerous microorganisms of many different kinds are hard at work in their fight for existence. At this early stage of the evolution of our planet the ground was still rather warm, and a large part of the water that now fills the ocean basins was still in the atmosphere, forming a thick layer of heavy clouds. No direct sunlight could penetrate to the surface of the Earth, and the life that was able to exist in this damp darkness must necessarily have been limited to certain micro-organisms that could live and grow entirely without sunlight. Some of these primitive organisms were using as their nourishment the remainder of the organic substances dissolved in ocean waters, whereas others grew accustomed to purely inorganic food. This second class of "mineral-eating" organisms can still be found in the so-called "sulphur and iron bacteria," which obtain their vital energy through the oxidation of inorganic compounds of sulphur and iron.* The activity of such bacteria plays quite an important role in the development of the Earth's surface; the iron bacteria, in particular, are probably wholly responsible for the thick deposits of bog iron ore, the main source of iron in the world.

But as time went on, the surface of the Earth grew cooler and cooler, more and more water was accumulated in the oceans, and the heavy clouds hiding the Sun were gradually thinned out. Under the action of the Sun's rays, which now were falling abundantly on the surface of our planet, the primitive micro-organisms were slowly developing the very useful substance chlorophyll to decompose the carbon dioxide of the air and using the carbon thus obtained to build up the organic substances needed for their growth. This possibility of "feeding on the air" opened up new horizons for the development of organic life and, combined with the *principle of collective life,*† culminated in the present highly developed and complex forms of the plant kingdom.

* The existence of such bacteria requires the presence of oxygen in the air, of course.

† I.e., the formation of complex organisms composed of many cells living together.

But some of the primitive organisms had chosen another way of development and, instead of getting their food directly from the air, of which there was plenty for everyone, preferred to obtain their carbon compounds in the "ready-to-use" form as produced by laborious plants. Since this parasitic manner of feeding was considerably simpler, the surplus energy of these organisms went into the development of an ability to move, which was quite necessary in order to get the food. Not being satisfied with a purely vegetable diet, the parasitic branch of living things began to eat one another, and the necessity of catching the game or of running away from pursuit developed their locomotive ability to the high degree characterizing the present animal world. The most primitive locomotion device, developed by the cephalopods (the "head-legged" animals) of the early Silurian period and retained until the present day by the squids, was based on the simple rocket principle. The spindle-shaped body of these animals is enclosed in a muscular fold of body wall known as the mantle, which leaves, however, some space that can be filled with water. Relaxation of the mantle permits the ingress of water into this cavity, and this water can be ejected in a powerful stream by a rapid muscular contraction, propelling the animal backward at rather high speed. The rocket principle did not prove to be very successful, however, and most organisms developed another method for propelling themselves through the lateral undulations of their elongated bodies. This mechanism reached a high degree of perfection rather early in the development of the inhabitants of marine and terrestrial waters, and only such reactionary animals as the squids still stick to the old principle. It may be noticed, though, that even the squids today possess two horizontal stabilizer fins, which are used for slow forward swimming by means of wave-like undulations.

It must be clear that swift motion through the water could hardly be achieved in the case of soft-bodied and easily deformable animals, since such motion requires rather rigid streamlined shapes, and the work of muscles can be much better transferred to the water through rigid "moving parts." Another reason for the development of rigid parts of the body was the necessity of protection from the attack of another "meat-eating" animal, as well as of better means for attacking the others. These "reasons," combined with the struggle for life and the survival of the fittest, finally resulted in the transformation of the soft jelly-like forms of the animal world into the heavily armoured types with powerful claws, such as the crabs and lobsters of today. The development of rigid parts turned out to be not only of great help to the animals themselves, but also to the modern palæontologists, who look for such remains in the pages of the "Book of Sediments." Whereas information about the soft-bodied animals of the past can be collected only from occasional imprints left by them on soft sand and, through mere chance, preserved to the present time (see Plate XVI), the animals with rigid shells or skeletons can be studied from their fossils almost as well as if they were living today. The whole historical period of the Earth and of life on its surface begins, properly speaking, from the time when animals began to develop rigid parts or bodies, and the museums of today are full of shells and skeletons permitting us to visualize the life forms of the distant past.

At the beginning of the Palæozoic era, some 500 million years ago, we find ocean life developed to a comparatively high level. Walking along the sandy ocean beaches of that time, we would find bunches of greenish seaweeds thrown up by the waves, and would be able to make a beautiful collection of sea shells in the very same way that so many people do today. Perhaps we would not be much surprised to see some strange-looking animals crawling through the wet sand and distantly reminding us of the horseshoe crabs of today. These animals, known as "trilobites" and representing one of the highest forms of life in this distant past, were probably developed from the soft-bodied segmented worms through the hardening of their skin and the fusion of separate segments into the head and the body. The first trilobites were rather small, not much larger than a pinhead, and had very rudimentary bodies with a badly developed eyeless head. Later, however, they made considerable progress, and the deposits of the Ordovician and Silurian periods contain the fossils of more than a thousand highly developed species. At the peak of their career the trilobites attained a length exceeding one foot and possessed very grotesque and highly ornamented bodies. This progress was followed, however, by a rapid decline, and the late Permian deposits contain only a few species of these interesting animals. The final blow to the existence of the trilobitic race was evidently dealt by the revolutionary changes on the Earth's surface, which, as we have seen, took place toward the end of the Permian period. The general elevation of the ground, the recession of the ocean, and the disappearance of interior water basins proved to be too much for these animals, which had ruled the surface of the Earth for more than 200 million years, and the race became completely extinct at the climax of the Appalachian revolution. Some side branch of the primitive trilobite stock must have survived all the dangers of the evolutionary past, however, and, becoming better adapted to surrounding conditions, carried their banners down to the present time. The latest representatives of this ancient branch are often served on our table under the names of shrimps, crabs, lobsters, etc.

Although the trilobites were exclusively marine animals, some of their close relatives known as "eurypterids" must have migrated up the rivers and into the interior lakes and developed the habit of living in fresh water. In fact, whereas the earliest eurypterids, small creatures only a few inches long, have been found in the marine deposits of the Late Cambrian period, the fossilized remains of the later and more developed representatives of this race (up to 10 feet long!) are very numerous in the deposits of continental waters formed 100 million years later.

Compared with the ocean, life in the fresh water of rivers and lakes is considerably less quiet and subject to much greater uncertainty. It must often have happened that such continental basins were cut off from their water supply and slowly dried up. Though most of the animals living in such basins must have necessarily perished, there was a bare chance that in some rare cases individuals could adjust themselves to the new conditions and continue their life on the dry land. These descendants of the eurypterid race, forced out of the water by the play of unfavourable circumstances, spread over the surface of the continents and became differentiated into various species of centipedes, millepedes, scorpions, spiders, etc. Later they took to the air, forming a large class of flying insects.

Returning to the ocean of the Early Palæozoic era, we

find another entirely different line of evolution. Instead of growing a rigid outer shell enclosing their soft body from without, a certain group of worms began to develop a stiff internal rod running along their entire body and evidently representing the prototype of the spinal cord in the fishes and higher vertebrates of today. A typical example of this transitional stage between ordinary worms and fish can be seen in the species known as "lancelet," which exists today and probably represents the direct descendants of the primeval fish stock. These animals of worm-like appearance differ, however, from ordinray worms in having a cartilaginous rod running along their entire length and minute "gill rods" supporting the side walls of the body. It is believed that the further development of this primitive skeleton culminated in the formation of a spinal cord and ribs, which distinguish all vertebrate animals from the more primitive ones. It is interesting to note in this connexion that in sharks, which represent the first "true" fish on record and which were in existence as early as the Silurian period, the continuous spinal rod is only partly replaced by the rings of the cartilage, and that complete replacement is attained only in the later fish species and in other higher vertebrates.

The exit of fishes from the water to dry land and their subsequent transformation into amphibians and reptiles were evidently due to the same combined causes as in the case of the more primitive invertebrates and probably proceeded along the same general lines. This exit must have taken place some time during the beginning of the latter part of the Palæozoic era, since the Upper Devonian and the Lower Carboniferous deposits contain some impressions that have been interpreted as the footprints of primitive amphibians. The fossilized skeletons of these amphibians, abundantly preserved in the Upper Carboniferous and Permian deposits, indicate that they belonged to the now extinct group of heavily armoured animals with solidly roofed skulls that earned for them the name of *stegocephalians* (i.e., "roof-headed" animals).

Some of these animals were only a few inches long, whereas others, especially those living during the latter part of the Carboniferous period, attained a length exceeding twenty feet. It is noteworthy that at least some species of stegocephalians had a third eye in the centre of their foreheads, which can also be found in a very rudimentary form in present-day amphibians and some higher vertebrates.*

But as in the case of so many other animal species, this blooming of the ancient amphibian kingdom was cut short by the increasing cold and dryness of the early stages of the Appalachian revolution, although a few of the species persisted well into the Triassic period. At present the amphibians are represented by comparatively few species of small-sized, humble animals such as frogs, toads, and salamanders. Some of the amphibians, however, must have completely lost their affinity for water and migrated to dry land, giving rise to a large reptilian kingdom that was destined to conquer the continents and rule unchallenged for the next 100 million years.

The early reptiles were lazy, long-bodied animals, many of them resembling the crocodiles of today. Others had very peculiar shapes, with high bony fins running along their backs and probably serving to fend them from un-

* The vestige of the "third eye" is now represented by the so-called pineal gland in the frontal part of the head.

expected attack (Plate XXI). All these primeval reptiles, like the reptiles of today, had their feet at their sides and were able to advance only by a rather slow sprawling across the land. Not until the beginning of the Mesozoic era did the reptiles develop an erect posture more adapted to running. This change of posture was probably one of the main reasons that enabled them to conquer the land and retain a dominant position throughout the long middle period of the Earth's history.

Parallel with the exit of animal life from the sea to dry land, and even probably preceding it somewhat, an analogous process was going on in the world of plants. Some of the terrestrial plants must have originated from seaweeds growing along the shore lines within the tidal zone and gradually growing accustomed to the periodic recession of the water. Others stemmed from the fresh-water vegetation that was forced to change its way of life owing to the drying out of the inland basins. The vegetation that first appeared on the surface of the continents was still very similar to the simpler forms previously living in the water, and was chiefly confined to the extensive shallow-water areas and marshlands that were so widespread during the inter-revolutionary periods. The forests of that distant past must have presented a very gloomy and fantastic appearance, consisting almost exclusively of ferns, horsetails, and club mosses, which grew into giant trees (Plate XX). All these were the primeval spore plants carrying neither blooming flowers nor fruits, and it took many hundred millions of years before the primeval plants reached the degree of development to which we are accustomed at present.

Since the vegetation of that time was mostly limited to

extensive marshlands, the trunks of the fallen forest giants were usually covered by a layer of water and, decomposing without access to the oxygen of the air, gave rise to rich coal deposits. This process of coal formation continued on an especially large scale during the middle part of the Late Palæozoic era, and among the geologists of today this period (lasting from 240,000,000 to 180,000,000 B.C.) is accordingly known as the *Carboniferous period.*

THE GREAT MIDDLE KINGDOM OF REPTILES

The Mesozoic era of the Earth's history is characterized by the splendid development of animal life on dry land and by the growth of small reptilian forms into giant monsters, known as *dinosaurs,* which challenge the most vivid imagination. As in the case of so many other forms of life, the race of dinosaurs started its existence in the early Triassic period as a group of comparatively small animals, not exceeding 15 feet in length, and developed in all its splendour only toward the end of the era. The early dinosaurs were rather slenderly built and had muscular hind legs and powerful tails, which aided in balancing the body as they ran. They must have been rather similar in appearance to today's Australian kangaroo, except for the absence of fur and the definitely reptilian shape of the head.

The further development of these primitive Triassic dinosaurs led to a great many other forms widely differing in size and in habits. The most terrifying representative of this group of animals was the so-called *Tyrannosaurus rex,* a huge carnivorous animal up to 20 feet in height and measuring about 45 feet from the tip of its nose to the end of its tail (Plates XVIIIA and XXIII). Compared with this "tyrannous king" of the Cretaceous period, the present king of beasts, His Majesty the Lion, is as harmless as a kitten.

In striking contrast to this monster of the past stood another representative of the kangaroo-like reptiles, known as the *ornithomimus.* It was small in stature and distantly resembled the ostriches of today. These peaceful animals probably fed on worms and small insects exclusively and, instead of teeth, had a horny beak resembling that of birds.

Besides this large group of dinosaurs, who travelled on their hind legs and tail and used their front paws exclusively for feeding purposes or fighting, there was another large branch which closely resembled the lizards of today, except in size. The members of this group probably were the most direct descendants of the early Permian reptiles (Plate XXI), and were less dynamic than their "two-legged" relatives. Travelling through the woods of the Jurassic period, one might easily run into *diplodocus* or his milk brother, the *brontosaurus,* weighing some 50 tons and measuring up to 100 feet from the tip of the nose to the end of the long tail, or into a giant *stegosaurus,* carrying a display of heavy armour-plate along its spine (Plate XXII).

There was no shortage of other kinds of horned reptiles, such as the giant *triceratops* (Plate XXIII), for example, or its humbler predecessor, the *protoceratops,* the eggs of which, through a fortunate play of chance, were preserved for the inquiring eyes of surprised present-day palæontologists (Plate XVIIIB).

In making our survey of the powerful Mesozoic kingdom of giant reptiles, we must not forget a large group which, for some reason unsatisfied with terrestrial life, returned to the seas and oceans and adjusted itself to the new conditions in much the same way as the seals, porpoises, and whales of today.* The waters of the Mesozoic era were full of different swimming reptiles constantly fighting among themselves for food. The most typical representatives of the marine reptiles of that time were the *ichthyosaurus,* rather resembling a fish in its general shape, and the rather clumsy *plesiosaurus,* which must, however, have been very successful in its fish-hunting expeditions, because of its long swan-like neck (Plate XXIV).

Among the most bizarre representatives of the great middle kingdom of reptiles were undoubtedly the *pterodactyls,* which formed the air force of the empire. These members of the reptile group, which took the air, had leathern wings, naked bodies, and sharp-toothed mouths (Plate XXV). During the Cretaceous period, when the kingdom of reptiles was at the peak of its development, these flying monsters reached their maximum size; specimens have been found measuring up to 25 feet from tip to tip of their outstretched wings.

The flying reptiles of the Mesozoic era represent the transitional stage to the birds of today, as becomes evident from an inspection of some skeletons found in the deposits of the Jurassic period (Plate XV). The creature that left us these fossilized remains is known as the *archæopteryx* and was a most peculiar combination of a typical flying reptile of the past and the ordinary bird of today. These half-reptiles, half-birds had bird-like plumage, although their sharp teeth, clawed wings, and long conical tails definitely betrayed their reptilian ancestry. One can hardly

* The reader is, of course, aware that the latter animals belong to the class of mammals that returned to the sea at some stage of their evolution.

desire any better specimen to demonstrate the continuity of evolution between such seemingly different groups of animals as reptiles and birds!

The kingdom of giant reptiles, with its innumerable representatives on the land, in the sea, and in the air, was certainly the most powerful and most extensive animal kingdom during the entire existence of life on the Earth, but it also had a most tragic and unexpected end. During a comparatively short period toward the end of the Mesozoic era the tyrannosaurus, stegosaurus, ichthyosaurus, plesiosaurus, and all the other "sauri" disappeared from the surface of the Earth as if wiped away by some giant storm,* leaving the ground free for miniature mammals that had waited for this opportunity for more than 100 million years.

The causes that led to such a sudden extinction of the most powerful animals that ever existed on the surface of our planet have remained rather obscure. It has often been suggested that the chief cause was the general elevation of the ground in the preparation for the Cainozoic revolution and the steady approach of more severe climatic conditions. But the extinction of intercontinental seas and marshlands could not have affected a large variety of dinosaurs, which were completely adapted to life on dry land, and we also know that many of the species, such as the pterodactyls, became extinct long before the climate became much cooler. It has also been suggested that the rising kingdom of mammals was directly responsible for the fall of the old reptilian empire. Nobody, of course, thinks that the tiny primitive mammal, not exceeding an ordi-

* At present the survivors of this mighty kingdom are represented by only a few species, such as crocodiles, alligators, and turtles.

nary rat in size, could have conquered the dinosaur in an open fight. But it is quite possible that, in their search for food, the mammals were eating up the dinosaur eggs, thus disastrously reducing the birth rate of these mighty animals. This hypothesis, however, does not explain all the facts, since a number of large reptiles, such as the ichthyosaurus, probably gave birth to living young, and these babies were sufficiently large to stand up for themselves.

Probably the most general hypothesis that can explain the fall of the reptilian kingdom and many other similar occurrences in other groups of animals is the assumption that the extinction of a race is due to the natural decrease of the birth rate in any old stock of living things. In fact, since each new generation within any given branch of organic evolution is produced by division of the genetic cells of previous generations, one may think that the hereditary properties carried over by the genus become more and more "diluted," and that the cells of the old stock gradually grow *"tired of division."*

Our present knowledge concerning the properties of the living cell and the process of its division is still very meagre, and there is no way of telling whether the above hypothesis is true or not. But, *a priori,* it does not seem at all impossible that such "exhaustion of living power" can take place, and that entire races of animals and plants can die out simply because they are getting much too old. Such a point of view would also be consistent with the *principle of recapitulation,* according to which the life of each individual repeats in its early embryonic stages all the phases of the development of its race. If the development of an individual parallels the development of the entire race, it would be logical to expect, conversely, that the race itself should die sooner or later in the same way as each of its separate members does.

THE "MILK AGE"

From the point of view of biology, the sentence about acquiring some habits "with one's mother's milk" makes very profound sense, since the presence of mammary glands producing the nourishing whitish liquid is the most fundamental characteristic of a large group of higher animal species to which we ourselves belong. Mammals vary widely in their traits and habits; some even lay eggs, as do the duckbills or the anteaters; but the unbreakable habit of giving good fresh milk to their babies binds them together into one well-defined group. The history of mammals probably dates as far back as the Late Palæozoic era, when the milk-producing organs were first developed in some small-sized reptiles that had become especially thoughtful about bringing up their babies. But through the dark periods of the Mesozoic era, when the land, sea, and air were under the permanent domination of giant reptiles, these humble child-loving animals had very little opportunity to develop. The deposits of the Jurassic period contain occasional remains of these archaic mammals, which were never larger than a very small dog and are most often found in association with the dinosaur, for which they must have been very tasty food. But the fact that these remains are found almost everywhere throughout the world (especially in Africa) indicates that this new type of life was very successful in the struggle for existence and contained in itself infinite possibilities for further development. It is interesting to note that the only place in the world where the fossils of primitive mammals are not found is the continent of Australia, the very same piece of land that is now characterized by the exclusive presence of such primitive mammals as duckbills, spiny anteaters, and kangaroos.* This fact may be considered a sign that the origin of mammals on this isolated continent took place much later and in an entirely independent way from the rest of the world, and it gives some support to the hypothesis that the similarity of many living forms may be connected rather with general rules of evolution in analogous surroundings than be the outcome of direct heredity (see the first section of this chapter). As for independent lines of evolution on different continents, one may also speculate regarding the relationship between the relative speed of evolution in different localities and the corresponding areas of available land. Since the progress of living things is achieved by the method of "trial and error," probably mostly error,† one should expect that the rate of such progress will be proportional to the number of individuals involved. Thus evolution should proceed faster on such extensive playgrounds as combined Eurasia and Africa, somewhat slower in the Americas, and much slower on the isolated little continent of Australia.

But we should not go too far into all these speculations, which can hardly be conclusively proved or disproved at the present time, and now let us return to the description of the progress of mammals. As was mentioned above,

* Kangaroos should be considered a rather primitive form of mammal, since, though they do not lay eggs, they give birth to their babies in not fully developed form and carry them in a skin pouch on the abdomen until they are completely formed.

† Of all the possible changes that can occur spontaneously in a living organism, comparatively few prove to be useful in the struggle for existence and are thus perpetuated by the process of natural selection.

these little animals were merely muddling through during hundreds of millions of years while all the *Lebensraum* on the Earth was entirely conquered by the reptiles. But with the sudden disappearance of the giant reptiles, which took place on the eve of the Cainozoic revolution, the mammals unexpectedly became the sole potentates of the continents, and rapidly developed to the full.

During the Eocene period, which opens the modern age in the history of the animal world, the mammalian kingdom was very extensive and had numerous representatives that can be readily recognized as the ancestors of the animals we know today. But *this primitive world was characterized by the extreme smallness of all the animal forms,* and it took a period of 40 million years for them to grow to their present size. The horses and camels of the Eocene period were about the size of a house cat, slender-bodied rhinoceroses were no larger than a pig, and the ancestors of today's elephants were hardly waist-high to a man. Of course, there was no man, not even a small one, but there were numerous miniature monkeys, which were probably already enjoying themselves by dropping coconuts from the tops of the trees. The beasts of prey were represented by the so-called *creodonts,* which later developed into two large branches of animals, the dog-like (dogs, wolves, bears) and the cat-like (cats, tigers, lions).

As time went on, some of the early mammalian forms died out, whereas others gradually developed and grew in size. By the time of the Miocene period, some 20 million years ago, horses had grown to the size of Shetland ponies, while the rhinoceros had already become a formidable beast, no longer to be got out of the way by a mere kick. But the mightiest animals of that time were certainly the giant boars, the *entelodonts,* which were as tall as an ox and had a skull 4 feet long (Plate XXVI). The ancestors of today's elephants also grew in size, and their trunks, almost unnoticeable in the early stages of development, grew longer and longer. On the continent of Europe and in Southern Asia, but not in America, one could occasionally meet nasty-looking great apes, known as dryopithecus and distantly related to the gorillas of today.

It must not be forgotten that up to the beginning of the Pleistocene glaciation (see Chapter VIII) the climate of the Earth was much milder, with food much more abundant, even in the northern latitudes, and that the animals now found only in the tropics then ranged over large areas of Europe, North America, and Northern Asia. In fact, the fossil remains found in the deposits of that time leave no doubt that elephants, rhinoceroses, hippopotami, lions, ordinary and extinct (sabre-toothed) tigers, and many other animals that are now found only in equatorial Africa were hunting for their food over the present sites of the cities of New York, Paris, Moscow, and Peiping.

When the large sheets of ice began advancing from the northern regions for the first time, slowly covering large areas of Europe and North America, the animal and plant life of this region was slowly pushed southward. Many species, which for one reason or another were unable to migrate farther south, perished from the increasing cold, while the others became accustomed to the new climate and developed long, warm furs protecting them from the frost of the polar winters.

Probably the most impressive sight of these chilly periods of the Earth's history was that of a family of heavily built long-tusked mammoths, covered with thick coats of brownish wool, making their way across the snow-covered continents (Plate XXVII). Although this race of giant hairy animals became extinct many thousands of years ago, frozen carcasses of some of them can still be found in the Siberian tundras. One member of an expedition of the Russian Academy of Sciences even ventured to eat a hamburger made of the frozen mammoth meat. Only the presence of a first-aid kit saved him from serious gastric distress.

In our general survey of the progress of life on the Earth we are now approaching the point where it is time to speak of ourselves, but since the development of man represents but a minute incident in the history of the Earth, we shall speak of it very briefly. There seems to be hardly any doubt that the man of today, or *Homo sapiens* ("clever fellow"), as we call ourselves in scientific discussions, developed from the primeval stock of anthropoid apes some time during the Pleistocene glacial epoch. One can imagine, for example, that during one of the successive advances of ice some group of these animals did not move south to continue its carefree existence in tropical forests, but remained where it was and was forced to get accustomed to the new, more severe conditions of life. The hardships that such an existence must have necessarily involved might easily have given the first impulse for the development of the primitive brains of these creatures, sending them along the path of discoveries and inventions characterizing the entire progress of the human race. In spite of the fact that primitive man lived in a much more recent epoch than the dinosaur, for example, the fossil remains left by him are very scarce and incomplete. Even though there has been intensive search for such remains, only very few have actually been found, and those are often nothing but a couple of disconnected bones or a fragment of a jaw. The representatives of these ancient

FIGURE 55
A picture of a mammoth cut into stone by a prehistoric artist on the wall of a cave at Combarelles, France.

human races, whose bones rest in the glass cases of our museums, giving a headache to ethnologists who try to guess their mutual relationship and their age, are usually called after the places where the discovery was made. Thus we have a "Java man," a "Peking man," a "Piltdown* (England) man," a "Heidelberg (Germany) man," a "Neanderthal (Germany) man," and a "Cro-Magnon (France)

* The skull of the "Piltdown" man was recently proved to be a fake and was dishonorably removed from its shelf in the British Museum.

man." The last of these had evidently reached a high stage of development and had pronounced artistic inclinations (Figure 55). Until recently there was no evidence of prehistoric man in America, but now we have evidence of a "Minnesota woman." In 1931 the skeleton of a woman was found at a depth beyond 9 feet in laminated glacial lake clay near Pelican Rapids, Minnesota, and from the age of these deposits it seems that this woman was drowned in the lake some 22,000 years ago.

Owing to the scarcity of these prehistoric human remains and the difficulty of establishing their exact age the revolutionary line of our race can be drawn only very vaguely, and it seems that the few known representatives belonged to some side branches rather than to the main stem of the *Homo sapiens* of today. In Figure 56 we give a schematic presentation of the time scale of the Pleistocene period and the probable chronological order of the known human fossils. As can be seen from the accompanying sketches, representing the reconstruction of primitive man, they were rather rough-looking fellows and can be called man only because they resembled us more closely than they resembled the apes. But the human race was making steady progress, with the size and activity of the brain increasing constantly;* and walking along the ocean beaches of today, we find not only seaweeds and shells as we would have a billion years ago but also the gay crowds of *Homo sapiens* cavorting and playing in the surf (PlateXXVIII).

* The brain of the great apes of the Miocene period had a volume of only 300 cubic centimetres, that of early Pliocene man (Java man) 985 cubic centimetres, and the brain of the man of today between 1300 and 1500 cubic centimetres.

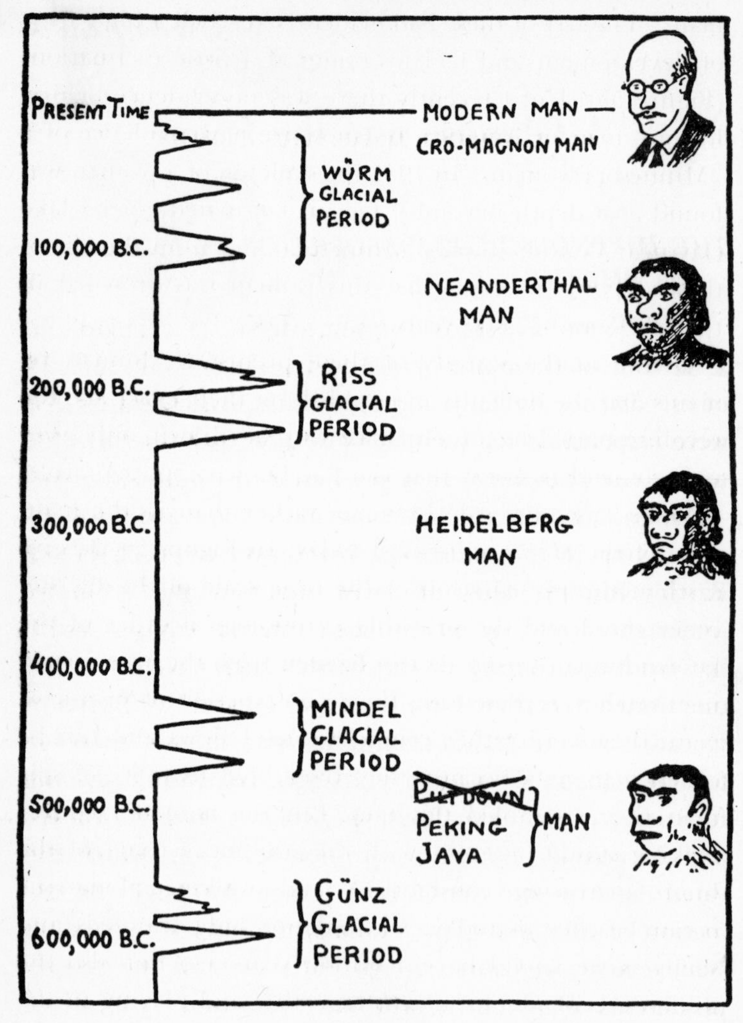

FIGURE 56
The evolution of man. (See note on page 220 concerning "Piltdown" Man.)

CHAPTER X

A Glimpse into the Future

THE IMPENDING CATASTROPHE OF MOUNTAIN FORMATION

AFTER we have studied in some detail the changes that took place on our planet during the two billion years of its existence and have understood the physical causes that were responsible for such changes, it is quite permissible to use our knowledge in a prediction of things to come.

As we have already indicated more than once, we are now living in the midst of a revolutionary epoch of the Earth's history, when its crust trembles and crumples under the action of accumulated internal stresses resulting from the cooling of the Earth's body. We have also mentioned that there have been two gigantic outbursts of volcanic and mountain-making activity in this epoch so far: one about 40 million years ago, responsible for the formation of the Himalayas, the Rockies, and the Andes, and the second one only 20 million years ago, which elevated the Alps and the Cascade Range. Although the formation of all these giant mountains represents quite an achievement, of course, it still falls short of the accomplishments of any of the previous revolutions. It therefore seems more than probable that the tectonic activity of the present revolution is far from complete, and that at some more or less remote future date humanity will witness catastrophes unprecedented in its past history.

Unfortunately, it is quite impossible to predict the date

of the next outburst or even to specify a "safety period" during which such a catastrophe can be guaranteed not to occur. To calculate the future behaviour of the Earth's crust, we must know the exact distribution of various materials in the entire thickness of the crust, its compressibility and ultimate strength, the distribution of existing stresses, and even the position of all cracks and other weak spots. But, even if an enormous amount of work by field geologists were able to give us all this information with the desired accuracy, the numerical calculations themselves would probably take thousands of years!

We are unable to predict the date of the catastrophe that hangs over our heads, nor can we say much about the symptoms that will announce its approach. These symptoms will consist of strong earthquakes, volcanic eruptions, and general motion of the ground, to be sure, but we do not know how violent these phenomena must become in order to be no longer considered routine adjustments of the crust, or how long before the main outburst they will begin to become prominent. On the other hand, we can be fairly certain that when the crumpling actually begins, the Earth will not be a very comfortable place to live on. In the localities immediately affected by mountain-forming activity the ground will be shaken by a wild *danse macabre,* and tremendous amounts of red-hot lava, erupted through the cracks opened in the crust, will spread over hundreds of thousands of square kilometres. Even in places far removed from the site of the new mountain birth violent earthquakes and most probably giant waves of the disturbed oceans will make life rather perilous.

The only consolation we can give the reader, who is probably terrified by this unpleasant perspective, is that it is not very likely that this catastrophe will happen during our lifetime. Since the entire revolutionary period extends over tens of millions of years, the probability that the outbreak will occur within, let us say, the next decade or the next century is negligibly small, much smaller than the probability of many other unpleasant events that can befall humanity.

THE NEXT GLACIAL PERIOD

Unable to give the timetable of the future tectonic catastrophe, we can, however, do much better in predicting the climate of the future and fixing the date for the next advance of polar ice on the continents that today are the chief sites of human culture. In Chapter VIII we saw that the periodicity of extensive glaciation seems to be connected mainly with purely astronomical events, and that the successive advances and retreats of ice sheets can be correlated with certain recurrent changes in the Earth's orbit and in the direction of its axis of rotation. Since a good astronomer experiences no difficulty in calculating the expected changes in these elements, even for many hundred thousand years ahead, the prediction of future ice ages becomes a comparatively easy task.

It will be remembered (Chapter IX) that there are three major factors affecting mean summer temperatures in the Northern and Southern Hemispheres: (1) *the elongation of the Earth's orbit;* (2) *the inclination of the Earth's axis of rotation to the plane of the orbit; and* (3) *the precision of the axis of rotation,* which, together with the *advance of the perihelion,* determines whether the Northern or Southern Hemisphere will be turned toward the Sun (i.e., have a summer season) when the Earth passes through

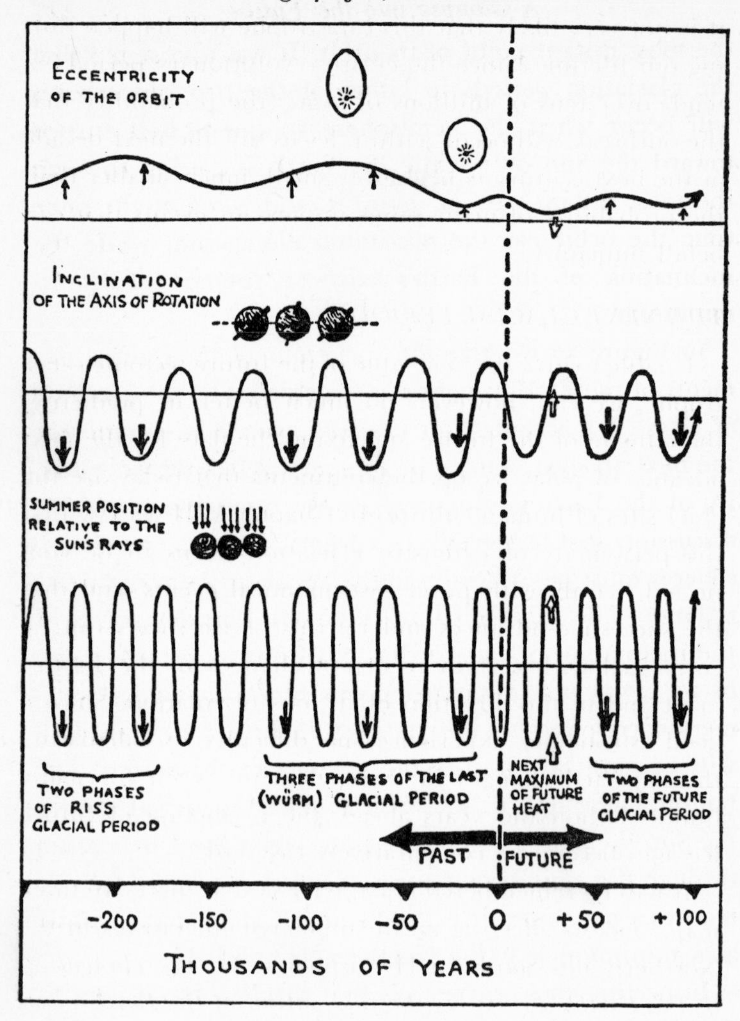

FIGURE 57
Diagram for predicting future glaciation periods and heat spells, constructed by the author.

the most distant point of its orbit. It was also stated that the glaciation periods in either of the two hemispheres will occur when the hemisphere in question is turned toward the Sun only while the Earth is passing through the most distant part of its orbit, and when at the same time the orbit has the maximum elongation, while the inclination of the Earth's axis of rotation is at its minimum.

In Figure 57 we give the variations of these three elements of the Earth's motion, as calculated by the methods of celestial mechanics, for the past 250,000 years and for the next 100,000 years. The top curve gives the eccentricity of the Earth's orbit, and, as we remember from the discussion in Chapter VIII, ice formation in both hemispheres must be especially intensive when the eccentricity is large. The middle curve represents the deviations of the inclination of the Earth's axis from its present value of 23° 27′ 30″ at different epochs. Since the coolest summers correspond to the smallest inclinations, glaciation will be most favoured at the minima of this curve. The bottom curve tells us which hemisphere is turned toward the Sun (i.e., has a summer season) when the Earth passes through the most distant point of its orbit; when the curve reaches a maximum it is the Southern Hemisphere, while at a minimum it is the Northern Hemisphere.

Inspecting these curves, we find that the conditions especially favouring ice formation occurred five times during the past 250,000 years, in groups of two and three. These are the same five recent glacial advances that we already recorded on the composite curve of summer temperatures in our hemisphere in Chapter VIII. In addition, we may note that the last glacial period in 25,000 B.C.

was not as severe as the previous ones, because at that time the eccentricity of the Earth's orbit was not very large, a conclusion that is in good agreement with geological data.*

Turning our attention to the future now, we find that *the conditions for the glaciation of the Northern Hemisphere will be again fulfilled in the years* A.D. *50,000 and* A.D. *90,000; and it must be expected that at these epochs much of North America and Europe will be covered by thick sheets of ice.* The eccentricity of the Earth's orbit at these epochs is expected to be somewhat larger than during the last glacial period but smaller than during the previous four. Thus *the two nearest advances of ice in this country will probably leave most of the United States untouched, although such cities as Boston, Chicago, and Seattle may find themselves at the very edge of a giant ice sheet covering all of Canada.* In Europe the ice descending from the Scandinavian highlands and brushing off the cities of Oslo, Copenhagen, Stockholm, and Leningrad will probably stop short before reaching London, Paris, and Berlin. It must be noted here, however, that although we can be reasonably sure about the motion of the ice sheets of the future, the fate of the cities of today must be considered rather dubious. The interval of time separating us from the next advance of ice is ten times longer than the time that has elapsed since ancient Egyptian civilization, and it may very easily happen that when the glaciers begin to descend from the polar regions all these cities will be of only historical interest to contemporary archæologists.

* In fact, during the last advance of ice on Europe only a comparatively small part of the continent and a few isolated places in the British Isles were actually covered by glaciers.

Further inspection of the curves indicating the climates of the future also shows us that *before the next advance of ice the climate of the Earth is bound to become much warmer than it is at present, and that the maximum will be reached about the year* A.D. *20,000.*

In Chapter IX we saw that tropical forests extended as far north as the Canadian border, and northern Germany in Europe, during the previous interglacial warm spells, and there is every reason to believe that the same situation will be repeated 20,000 years from now. This future extension of tropical vegetation, accompanied, of course, by the northward migration of all kinds of animals now found only in the equatorial regions of Africa or South America, will be probably even greater than during former interglacial stages, since, as we can see from Figure 57, the eccentricity of the Earth's orbit will reach an unprecendentedly low value. Thus, we may expect that in the year A.D. 5000 the climate of Boston, for example, will resemble that of Washington, D.C., in A.D. 10,000 that of New Orleans, in A.D. 15,000 that of Miami, and in A.D. 20,000 that of the West Indies. Later on, the temperature changes will be reversed and by A.D. 50,000 the surroundings of Boston will resemble those of fur posts on Baffin Bay.

THE END OF THE CAINOZOIC AND THE FOLLOWING CHAPTERS

Looking still further ahead into the future history of our planet, we can expect the same monotonous regularity that characterized its past. For the first tens of millions of years, while the mountains of today will be still standing on the surface of the continents, with new mountains rising in the catastrophes of crust-crumpling, the surface of the Earth will look much as it does now, and periodic glacial advances of smaller or larger intensity will alternate with interglacial warm spells. Later on, the present revolutionary activity will slowly die out, and the laborious work of rain will finally obliterate the last hill on the surface of the Earth. Continental surfaces will become flat and uninteresting, and large areas will be inundated by ocean water, forming extensive shallow seas. The climate will become mild and uniform, and one will be able to travel from Florida to Canada without changing a suit of clothes.

These flat inter-revolutionary continents will still be dominated by the representatives of the mammalian kingdom, but these will probably increase in size considerably. As we have seen in the previous chapter, all the animal races that have dominated the world during one era or another of the Earth's history constantly grew in size up to the point where they became extinct, and there appears to be no reason to believe that the present size of living mammals represents the upper possible limit. It may be that elephants, which are already much too large even today, will be unable to continue their development and will vanish from the face of the Earth (they are already vanishing!), but all the other animals, including man, seem to be quite capable of further growth. Thus, one can easily imagine a picture of the "Palæontological Museum of the Year A.D. 80,000,000," where visitors 10 or 15 feet tall inspect the fossil skeleton of a milk-wagon horse, which seems to them no larger than a dog.

But one should not go too far along the path of fantasy, even if it is based on scientific fact, and here we close the door on the discussion of the future extinction of our human race, which may take place, for example, simply because of the degeneration of the cells and the corresponding drastic reduction of the birth rate.

There is also no way of guessing which breed of animals will take the throne of the "Dictator of the Earth," and we may well look with suspicion and a feeling of rivalry at any small creature that may now be crawling at our feet!

Returning to the Earth itself, we may expect it to grow a thicker and thicker solid crust, which will some time become sufficiently strong to withstand any further stresses. At this stage of development the periodic revolutionary crumpling of the Earth's surface layers will be finally checked, and after the last mountains have been washed away by rain, the surface of the continents will remain for ever flat and smooth. Only the original division into continental massifs and ocean basins will remain intact, as a permanent memory of the birth of a daughter to our planet.

THE FATE OF THE MOON

As we have seen at the beginning of this book, the Moon was formed about five billion years ago from a giant tidal bulge produced on the primitive Earth by solar attraction and increased beyond the limit of structural strength by accidental resonance. After the first rapid jerk away from the maternal body of the Earth the Moon continued its recessive motion, at the same time slowing down the rotation of our globe. Since its birth the distance of the Moon has increased from zero to its present value of 385,000 kilometres, whereas the length of the Earth's day increased from 4 to 24 hours.

But the tides continue to rise twice daily in the oceans of our planet, and the process of the recession of the Moon and the lengthening of the terrestrial day is steadily going on. Using the same methods as in the case of the past history of the Moon, we find that *about 20 or 30 billion years from now the Moon is due to reach its maximum distance from the Earth (about 20 per cent farther than now), and that at that epoch the day will be as long as the lunar month, each equalling 47 of our present days.*

That state, in which the Moon hangs immovably above one of the terrestrial hemispheres, cannot represent the final word in the relations between Mother Earth and its daughter, however, since there still remains the influence of the Sun. Detailed analysis of the situation shows that under the action of solar tidal friction the Earth is due to continue the slowing down of its rotation, toward the ultimate goal of making the length of the day equal a year, whereas *the Moon must be slowly dragged back toward the Earth.*

This return of the Moon, however, can be expected to be a process several times slower than its recession, for the solar tides acting in this case are smaller than the lunar tides that are now pushing the Moon away. *Thus it may take more than 100 billion years before our satellite comes close to the Earth and, broken to pieces by strong gravitational forces, forms something like a Saturn ring around our planet.* It must be borne in mind that in making these estimates of time the assumption was used that the tides in terrestrial oceans will always continue their work in the same way as they do at present.

In the next section, however, we shall see that *such an assumption can hardly be taken as valid.* Study of the future evolution of the Sun indicates that this "central heating plant" of our planetary system will undergo important changes within the next 10 billion years. It can be expected that toward the end of that period the heat of the Sun will increase to such an extent that our oceans will be evaporated almost completely, and that later on the Sun will rapidly cool down again, freezing to the very bottom any bodies of water still left on the Earth. Thus it seems that *the future work of ocean tides is limited to less than the next 10 billion years, during which they will even be unable to push the Moon away to its maximum possible distance.* Of course, when the oceans disappear, or are completely frozen, there will always remain the action of the body tides in the Earth. Since body tides are considerably lower, however, *and are subject to much smaller friction, the time scale of the future behaviour of the Moon will be lengthened by a factor of 100 or even more.*

THE SUN WILL CLOSE THE SHOW

In our studies of the origin and the evolutionary development of the Earth we have seen that its entire history is closely and inseparably connected with the central body of our planetary system, the Sun. We have also seen that throughout that time, when important changes were taking place on the surface of our planet, the Sun itself remained virtually unchanged, and that its radiation, in particular, could not have varied more than a few per cent. But everything must come to an end, and in spite of its evidently tremendous internal resources, our Sun is due to cool down sooner or later. The problem of solar energy sources has always been among the most exciting problems of science, but its solution has become possible only within the last few years.

We now know that *the energy radiated by the Sun, as well as by other stars, is produced by the transformation of chemical elements that is steadily going on within its hot interior.* The "alchemic fuel" that is responsible for the production of heat in the interior of the Sun is now recognized to be the familiar gas hydrogen, and the "product of combustion" is represented by helium, which was first discovered in the solar atmosphere. The transformation of solar hydrogen into helium, accompanied by the liberation of tremendous amounts of subatomic energy, does not go on by itself, however; it requires some catalytic agents, which in this case are found to be the atoms of carbon and nitrogen.

The amount of hydrogen contained in the body of the Sun at present is estimated to be about 35 per cent by weight, and from the rate of consumption necessary to support solar radiation, we find that *the supply of this "alchemic fuel" suffices for roughly another 10 billion years.* A more detailed study of the processes taking place in the solar interior also leads to the conclusion that the steady decrease of the amount of "hydrogen fuel" will only cause more violent "combustion" of what is still left, so that, contrary to ordinary expectations, *the Sun must become more and more brilliant from century to century.* This progressive increase of solar activity is taking place very slowly, of course, and it has been calculated that, during the entire geological period of the last two billion years, it has raised the surface temperature of our Earth by only a few degrees. However, during the next 10 billion years that separate us from the epoch of the death of the Sun, the progressive increase of luminosity will continue steadily, and *toward the end of that period the Sun will be about a hundred times brighter than it is now. By that time the surface of our planet will be heated to about the boiling point of water, the oceans will have evaporated, and the Earth's atmosphere will be heated to such a degree that most of it will probably escape into interplanetary space* (compare the discussion in Chapter IV).

No life will be possible on the Earth any longer, and all its inhabitants will either perish of the heat or be forced to emigrate to some more distant planets, provided, of course, that they are highly intelligent beings and have solved the problem of interplanetary communication.

After this maximum effort, similar to that of a runner approaching the finish line, our Sun, deprived of the last ounce of its "alchemic fuel," will finally turn toward its deathbed.

It was believed until quite recently that this last stage of solar evolution would consist of a comparatively quiet contraction of its giant gaseous body, accompanied by a rapid decrease of its emitted radiation. However, investigations carried out by the author at the time he was preparing this book indicate that *even when "walking the last mile" our Sun will once more demonstrate its might and will burst into a brilliant display of fireworks.* In fact, it can be shown by the analysis of the physical processes that must take place within any star contracting toward its death, that *at a certain stage the steady contraction*

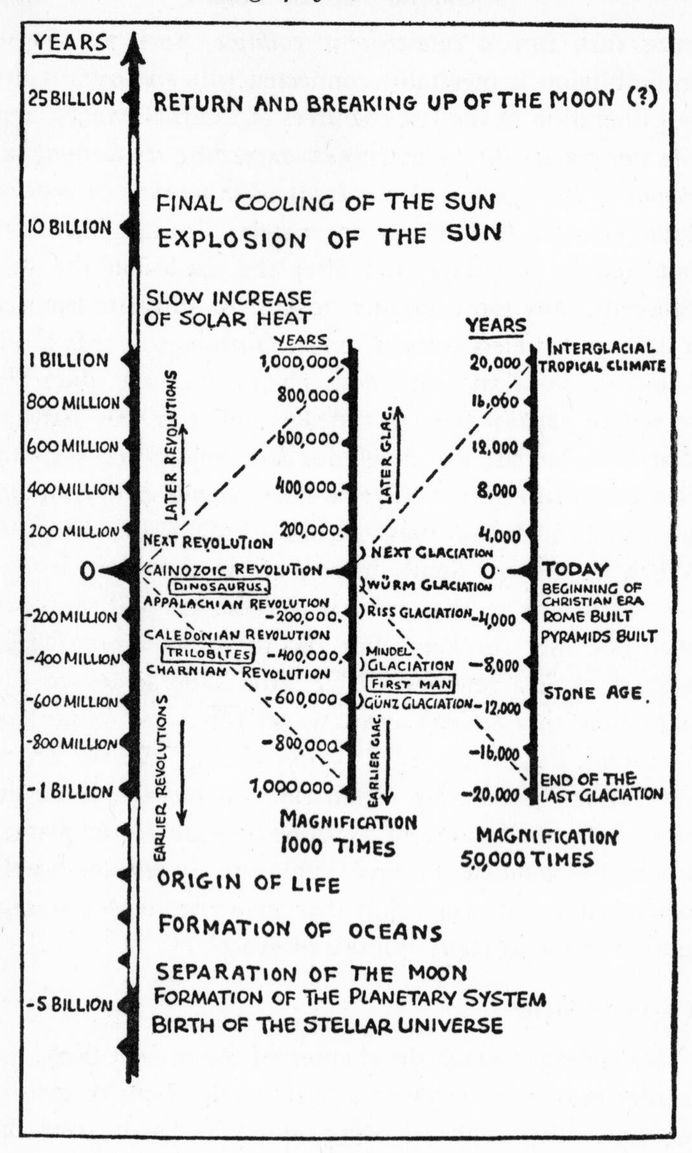

FIGURE 58

Comparative chart of past and future events. Two successive magnifications were used in order to give finer details.

must turn into a catastrophic collapse. Such a collapse into oblivion is inevitably connected with the instantaneous liberation of the last resources of internal energy, and *the star bursts into a brightness exceeding its normal luminosity by a factor of hundreds of thousands or even a billion (in the case of very heavy stars).* But this last effort lasts only a few days, and after the explosion the star proceeds, only more rapidly, toward its ultimate state of a dark and lifeless celestial body. Outbursts of this kind, known as nova and supernova phenomena, are often observed in various stars in the sky, and it is only natural that a similar fate will befall our Sun. Since, however, our Sun is still full of life and, as we have mentioned, contains plenty of "alchemic fuel," it has a long life to live yet. When its collapse finally takes place in the year A.D. 10,000,000,000 or so, the outburst of radiation will probably melt not only our Earth but also the other more distant planets. And a few years later, after "the smoke of the explosion" has cleared away, we will find the dying Sun surrounded by its family of rapidly cooling planets. There will be no observer to watch this sad picture, however, since, even if life were to continue on some of the planets up to the moment of final explosion, it will be surely destroyed by the same Sun that gave rise to it and supported it for so many billions of years.

CONCLUSION

Struggling through the chapters of the present book, the reader must have received a fairly comprehensive picture of the evolution of our cosmic ship, the Earth, from the very beginning of its existence as the gaseous piece of matter condensed from the primordial material which surrounded the Sun during its early days, down to the very end, when it will be melted again in the last desperate explosion of its dying parent. In order to refresh the reader's mind, the chronological charts in Figure 58 summarize the most important events of the Earth's past and future evolution. These charts may also serve to point out the unimportance of human history, compared with even such a tiny bit of cosmic matter as our little Earth.

Index